VACATION STATIONS

Review Program for Reading, Math, and Language Arts

WHEELS WESTWARD

For 1st Grade Going into 2nd

BOB JONES UNIVERSITY PRESS ▪ GREENVILLE, SOUTH CAROLINA 29614

www.bjup.com

NOTE:

The fact that materials produced by other publishers may be referred to in this volume does not constitute an endorsement of the content or theological position of materials produced by such publishers. Any references and ancillary materials are listed as an aid to the student or the teacher and in an attempt to maintain the accepted academic standards of the publishing industry.

VACATION STATIONS
Wheels Westward

Project Management
David Harris

Project Coordinator
Joyce Garland

Writer
Diana Simms

Elementary Authors Project Director
Vicky Burr

Project Editor
Carolyn Cooper

Cover and Book Design
Elly Kalagayan

Computer Formatting
Peggy Hargis

Contributing Writers
Eileen Berry
Joyce Garland
Joan Hill
Christine Kuhr
Charlotta Pace

Photo Acquisition
David Palmer

Production Design
Holly Gilbert
Wendy Searles

Typesetting
Janet Davis
Jennifer Hearing
Jeremy Larson

Illustration Coordinator
Mary Ann Lumm

The following individuals have contributed to the illustrations included in this book.

Eden Anderson	Preston Gravely	John Muessen
Julie Bunner	Dyke Habegger	Kathy Pflug
Paula Cheadle	Jim Hargis	Lynda Slattery
Johanna Ehnis	Jeremy Jantz	Sanela Tutaris
Justin Gerard	Stefanie Kubina	Yoo-Kyung Julie Yang
Cory Godbey	Joel Leineweber	

Cover Photo Credits: PhotoDisc, Inc.
Unusual Films

ISBN 1-57924-592-7

15   14   13   12   11   10   9   8   7   6   5   4

...CONTENTS...

··· Dear Parents ···

Thank you for selecting **Vacation Stations**, a program that will help you become more involved in your child's education. Your choice clearly shows that you believe the right education is both important and valuable.

The materials in **Vacation Stations** allow you to extend your influence in your child's education. Since many children lose valuable skills over the summer months—the very skills they will need as they begin the next school year—it is important to find engaging ways to strengthen their skills while they are away from the classroom.

Vacation Stations has been developed to help students systematically review grade level materials in ten weeks. It is designed to help review math, reading, and language art skills in only fifteen minutes of independent work a day. It focuses on the key concepts in each discipline.

Vacation Stations is designed to be a summer program that will reinforce and review the previous year's work. However, this program can also be an effective tool for reviewing material throughout the school year. We hope you enjoy this journey with your child.

Travel Notes

Itinerary

Schedule a time for your child's practice each day. Having a consistent time set aside will help your child remember to do the activities. Each day's two-page assignment should take approximately fifteen minutes.

Luggage

Provide adequate supplies. To complete the activities, your child will need a pencil, a sixteen-count box of crayons, and, of course, his **Vacation Stations** book. Additional writing and drawing paper will allow your child to extend the activities provided in his book. Store the supplies in a specific place, such as a desk or box that can be easily moved.

Destination

Designate a place for your child to work. Having a specific place will provide consistency and will encourage your child to stay focused as he practices each day. If possible, choose a location away from distractions.

Travel Agent

Oversee your child's work. Some activities will be easy; others may provide a challenge. Suggest ways to complete difficult sections and encourage your child to try everything. Allow him to use the answers provided in the back of the book to self-check his work. Help him make corrections to reinforce the skills he practiced.

Travel Log

Direct your child to record his progress. A chart provided at the beginning of each week helps your child see his successful completion of the activities. In addition, a log is provided to encourage independent reading.

Station Stops

 As your child "travels" to each station, he will practice specific skills.

Fact Harbor ▸ Reviews addition and subtraction facts. The number and design of the equations are appropriate to the level of the child. Fact families are also included as a part of this station.

 MATH JUNCTION ▸ Focuses on computation and place-value skills. The computation activities are kept short to encourage the success of every child. A few problems done correctly are more effective than many problems done carelessly.

Math Beacon ▸ Reviews the many other concepts in mathematics. Both metric and customary measurement standards are reinforced. Also, time, money, fractions, graphs, and geometry are included as part of this station.

▸ Each week's work includes a reading selection with questions. This selection reinforces the book's theme and provides questions to encourage higher thinking skills. In addition to this page, other stations also review reading and language arts skills.

 ▸ Includes a variety of reading concepts. Comprehension and vocabulary are the main focus of most of the sections of this station.

 ▸ Reviews phonics and word analysis skills. Both vowel and consonant sounds are reviewed. Prefixes, suffixes, and syllabication are also part of this station.

 ▸ Encourages your child to write. Composition is an important skill. Each week your child is given an idea for writing. Though space to write is provided in the book, paper should be available to encourage further writing.

 ▸ Reinforces the basic skills needed for gathering information. Alphabetizing, using reference materials, applying map skills, following directions, and classifying are a few of the concepts reviewed at this station.

 ▸ Reviews grammar and sentence constructions. A review of the parts of speech, capitalization, punctuation, and kinds of sentences makes up this station.

 ▸ Provides a good finish for the week by giving your child an activity that is lighter and more entertaining.

Help Your Child
Read Independently

Many parents ask the question "How can I help my child become a good reader?" Reading outside the instructional setting is essential for success. Your influence in the following ways may make a lifelong difference in your child's reading.

Read to your child. Children of all ages benefit as they listen to an adult read. When a child hears material that is *above his own reading level*, his vocabulary is stretched and enriched. He begins to notice the more interesting syntax patterns that he will later encounter in his own personal reading.

Provide a variety of reading materials for your child. Children who are surrounded by books, magazines, and reference materials are more likely to do independent reading than are children who have only limited reading materials available to them.

Visit the library with your child. Help your child select easy, interesting books for his independent reading and more difficult, appealing books for you to read aloud to him.

Provide a model for your child. A child who sees a parent reading is more likely to be a reader himself. Let your child see you reading a variety of material so that he recognizes the many ways that reading is used each day.

Emphasize silent reading before oral reading. Encourage your child to always read silently before reading aloud. Make sure he understands that he can ask for help with words as he reads silently. A child should need only a little help if the book he is reading is appropriate for his reading level. A child benefits more from an easier book that he can successfully read than from a book that causes frustration because it is too difficult.

PROGRESS

PAGES Circle a for every page completed.

Parent's Initials

DAY 1 •

DAY 2 •

DAY 3 •

DAY 4 •

DAY 5 •

READING Color a for every 10 minutes of reading you do.

DAY 1	DAY 2	DAY 3	DAY 4	DAY 5
☆	☆	☆	☆	☆
☆	☆	☆	☆	☆
☆	☆	☆	☆	☆

Fact Harbor

Solve each fact. Write the facts that equal 12 inside the rope.

3 + 7 =

6 + 3 =

8 + 7 =

6 + 7 =

3 + 9 =

8 + 4 =

12

4 + 7 =

7 + 5 =

4 + 9 =

2 + 9 =

4 + 8 =

6 + 5 =

Word Wayside

Color the words.

or as in = blue

ar as in  = green

ir as in = orange

stork	part	stir	horse
scarf	girl	port	far
short	firm	farm	shirt
barn	twirl	cord	torn

· · · · · DAY 1 · · · · ·

Write the number of tens and ones.

56 = __5__ tens __6__ ones

40 = _____ tens _____ ones

39 = _____ tens _____ ones

67 = _____ tens _____ ones

99 = _____ tens _____ ones

READING OUTPOST

Read the word families. Cross out the word that does *not* belong.

game	snake	made	gate
shame	rake	skate	late
lane	bake	shade	lake
flame	gate	grade	plate

Stagecoach Stations

How would you have traveled in the Old West? You might have ridden in a stagecoach. On a long trip you might have stopped at a home station.

At a home station travelers could get meals. At some stations the meals were good. At other stations the meals were not good. Travelers could also get a place to sleep. Often the beds were hard. Sometimes the rooms were unclean. But tired travelers were thankful for a place to sleep.

Circle the correct answer.

1. How might you have traveled in the Old West?
   (by bus, by stagecoach)

2. Where did stagecoaches stop?
   (home stations, coach stations)

3. Were the meals always good at a station?
   (no, yes)

4. What word means not clean?
   (hard, unclean)

5. Why do you think the travelers were thankful for any bed and room?
   (They were very tired. They didn't like clean rooms.)

Write the time.

:		:		:		:

:		:		:		:

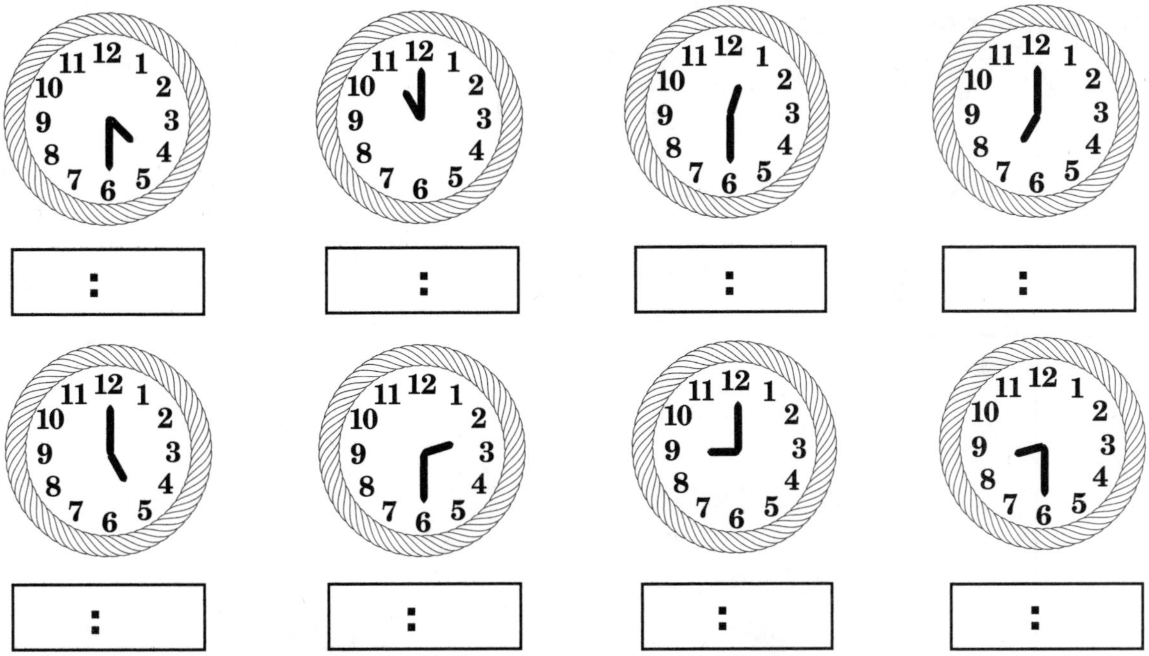

Word Wayside

Clap the syllables and color the correct number of ☺s.

boxes	☺ ☺	wishbone	☺ ☺
rattle	☺ ☺	fish	☺ ☺
bone	☺ ☺	saddle	☺ ☺
cracker	☺ ☺	buckle	☺ ☺
rope	☺ ☺	branding	☺ ☺
cowboy	☺ ☺	west	☺ ☺

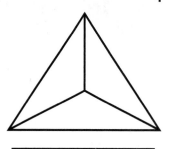 **Math Beacon**

Count the equal parts.
Write the number of equal parts.

 ___ parts

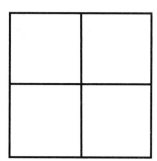 ___ parts

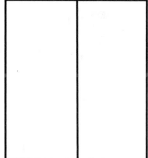 ___ parts

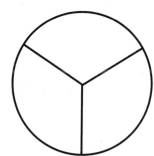 ___ parts

READING OUTPOST

Color the barrels the correct color.

brown

orange

blue

green

yellow

black

purple

red

····· DAY 3 ·····

Solve the facts.

4	8	14	5	11
− 3	− 0	− 9	− 1	− 7

4	8	6	15	12
− 4	− 5	− 2	− 8	− 9

Word Wayside

Circle the correct word for each sentence.

1. Mark plays in the   hand   sand .

2. The water in the   bond   pond   is dirty.

3. I can hear the pig   grunt   hunt .

4. Mother gave me the   rink   ring .

5. The bird hurt his   wink   wing .

READING OUTPOST

Read the sentences.

The cowboy bought a saddle for his horse, Jake. He put the saddle on Jake. The cowboy sat in the saddle. He rode out of town.

Color the correct answers.

1. What was the horse's name? Jumper   Jake

2. What did the cowboy buy? a rope   a saddle

3. What did the cowboy put on Jake? a saddle   a spur

4. Where did the cowboy ride? in town   out of town

STUDY SKILL
HEADQUARTERS

Number the words in alphabetical order.

a b c d e f g h i j k l m n o p q r s t u v w x y z

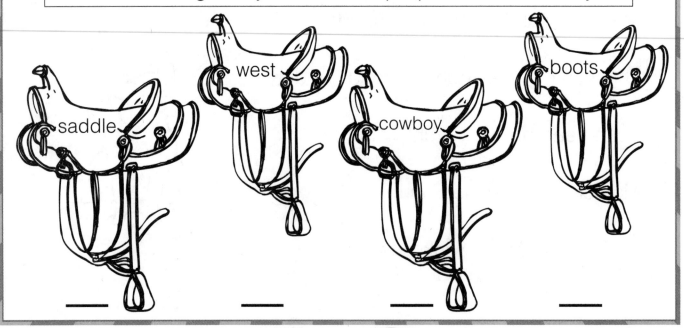

saddle   west   cowboy   boots

___   ___   ___   ___

Math Beacon

Circle the correct answer.

Quart = cup cup cup cup	yes	no
Pint Pint = Quart	yes	no
Pint = cup cup cup	yes	no

Writer's Nook

Finish writing the story.

If I were going on a trip out West, I would

Math Beacon

Color the shape that is the same size and shape as the first one.

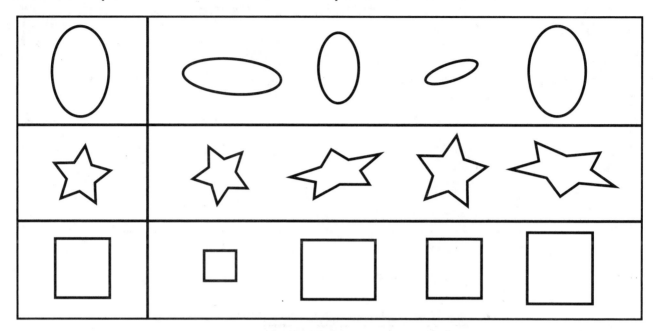

LANGUAGE
LODGE

Color each contraction and its matching words the same color.

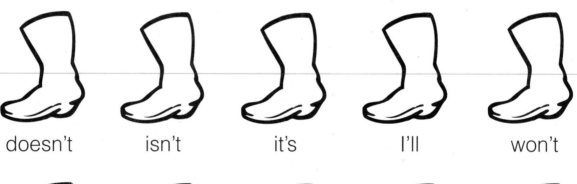

doesn't   isn't   it's   I'll   won't

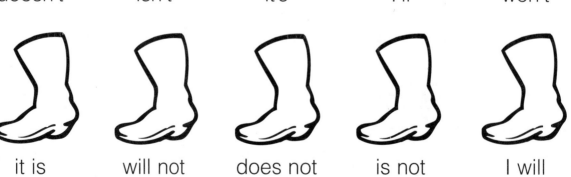

it is   will not   does not   is not   I will

Draw a picture of the sentence.

The cowboy fed his horse.

Fact Harbor

Complete each family of facts.

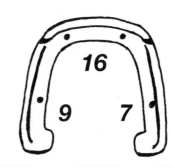

$7 + 5 = 12$

$5 + 7 = 12$

$12 - 7 = 5$

$12 - 5 = 7$

STATION BREAK

Find the words in the puzzle.

horse   saddle   cowboy   boot   brand   lasso   spurs   ranch

a	l	s	k	f	k
c	c	e	z	q	x
b	o	o	t	d	s
v	w	g	h	g	a
b	b	r	a	n	d
n	o	b	u	f	d
h	y	u	l	w	l
o	h	t	j	b	e
r	a	n	c	h	l
s	h	g	n	j	a
e	s	p	u	r	s
c	v	o	m	f	s
t	s	h	j	r	o

·· P R O G R E S S ··

Week Two

PAGES ▷ Circle a for every page completed.

Parent's Initials

DAY 1 •

DAY 2 •

DAY 3 •

DAY 4 •

DAY 5 •

READING ▷ Color a ☆ for every 10 minutes of reading you do.

DAY 1	DAY 2	DAY 3	DAY 4	DAY 5
☆	☆	☆	☆	☆
☆	☆	☆	☆	☆
☆	☆	☆	☆	☆

Fact Harbor

Color the names for 11 green.
Color the names for 10 orange.

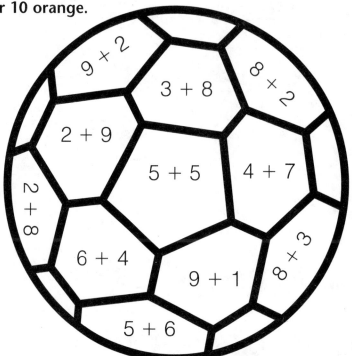

Word Wayside

Circle the correct word.

1. Tim was $\begin{array}{l}\text{shading}\\\text{shadeing}\end{array}$ his eyes from the sun.

2. Abby is $\begin{array}{l}\text{tapping}\\\text{taping}\end{array}$ the box shut.

3. The child was $\begin{array}{l}\text{hoping}\\\text{hopping}\end{array}$ to ride the horse.

4. I can ride my bike fast on the $\begin{array}{l}\text{sloping}\\\text{slopping}\end{array}$ road.

5. Lindy is $\begin{array}{l}\text{riding}\\\text{ridding}\end{array}$ the skateboard.

Circle the set with fewer objects.

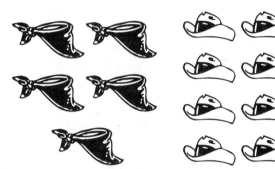

READING OUTPOST

Draw a line to match the word with the picture.

clown

plow

mouse

crown

house

brow

Prairie Dog Chase

Dale and Paula watched the hole. Just then a prairie dog popped up. "There's one," shouted Dale to Paula. "Let's catch it."

The children ran to the hole. Down went the prairie dog. A few yards away up popped a prairie dog. "Is that the same one?" asked Paula. "It sure is fast."

Time and time again the children raced to a hole. But every time the prairie dog went down just as they got there. Somewhere else a prairie dog would poke its head out of its hole.

"They seem to be playing a game with us," said Dale in a tired voice. "I think they won."

Answer the questions.

1. Circle who is watching the hole.

2. What happens after the prairie dog goes down its hole?

   _____

   _____

   _____

3. What kind of children's game is this like? _____

   _____

   _____

4. Why does Dale say the prairie dogs have won?

   _____

   _____

Math Beacon

Write the value of each coin.

penny   nickel   dime

| 1¢ | ¢ | ¢ |

Write the total value as you count.   **Total Value**

10¢   15¢   ___   ___   ___   ___

___   ___   ___   ___   ___   ___

Word Wayside

Color the box that has an object with the same short-vowel sound.

ă	ĕ	ĭ	ŏ	ŭ
fan	bee	bike	fox	bug
snake	tent	crib	coat	flute

· · · · · DAY 2 · · · · ·   17

Math Beacon

Color one-third of each shape.

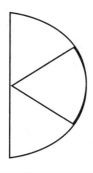 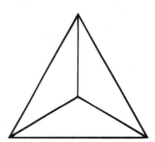 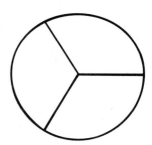

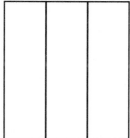 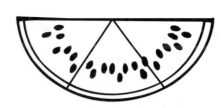 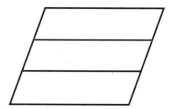

Reading Outpost

Circle the opposites.

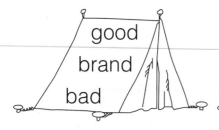

good
brand
bad

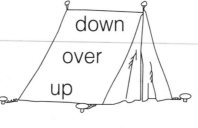

down
over
up

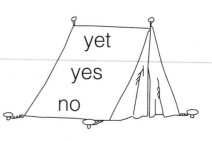

yet
yes
no

gave
brook
took

day
noon
night

wet
dry
we

Color the correct oval.

12−6 = 7 5 6

13−4 = 8 9 7

10−4 = 6 8 7

12−4 = 7 8 9

11−6 = 6 7 5

10−6 = 4 3 5

9−2 = 7 6 8

12−3 = 8 10 9

8−5 = 2 3 1

11−4 = 6 8 7

10−7 = 3 2 4

11−8 = 2 3 4

Word Wayside

Circle the beginning or ending *st*.

st  st st  st

st   st st   st

st   st st   st

st   st st   st

Read the sentences. Mark the correct answers.

1. The horse wanted hay.
   - ◯ He was not hungry.
   - ◯ He was hungry.

2. Father cuts the logs for the fireplace.
   - ◯ The logs are too big.
   - ◯ The logs are too small.

3. Anna planted the seeds.
   - ◯ She wanted fish.
   - ◯ She wanted flowers.

4. Ellen read the books many times.
   - ◯ She likes to read.
   - ◯ She does not like to read.

STUDY SKILL
HEADQUARTERS

Follow the directions.
1. Write your first name.
2. Draw a picture of yourself.
3. Put a cowboy hat and boots on your picture.

Me

Circle the correct measurement tool.

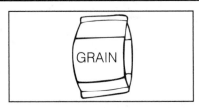 

Writer's Nook

Finish writing the story.

If I lived in a tepee, I would _____

_____

_____

_____

_____

_____

_____

_____

Solve each problem using the place-value frame.

Tens	Ones
3	2
+ 2	4

Tens	Ones
7	4
+ 2	3

Tens	Ones
6	3
+ 3	5

Tens	Ones
4	3
+ 4	3

Tens	Ones
2	8
+ 4	1

Tens	Ones
1	2
+ 8	6

LANGUAGE LODGE

Circle the letters that should be uppercase. (There are two in each sentence.)

1. tuesday is tony's birthday.

2. bill finley is our bus driver.

3. dad gave me a new bible.

4. i will visit you on thursday.

5. ann's birthday is in september.

6. jason likes to play with samuel.

7. our school starts in august.

Draw a picture of the sentence.

The cowboy cooked his food over a fire.

Fact Harbor

Complete each family of facts.

5	+	6	=	11

Circle the odd numbers. Draw a line to connect the odd numbers and help the prairie dog get to his hole.

3   5

2

6

4   1

8   14

7   11   10

13   12

9   15

Did you know that prairie dogs are also called ground squirrels?

PROGRESS

Week Three

DAY 1 ·

DAY 2 ·

DAY 3 ·

DAY 4 ·

DAY 5 ·

READING Color a ☆ for every 10 minutes of reading you do.

DAY 1	DAY 2	DAY 3	DAY 4	DAY 5
☆	☆	☆	☆	☆
☆	☆	☆	☆	☆
☆	☆	☆	☆	☆

Fact Harbor

Complete the charts.

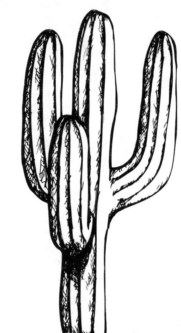

Add	6
5	
7	
9	
8	
6	
3	

Add	9
5	
8	
4	
6	
7	
9	

Word Wayside

Circle the correct word.

1. I gave the toy / joy to Sammy.

2. The flower was planted in the soil / coil .

3. The girl showed me the new coin / join .

4. You may have your choice / voice of snack.

5. The water began to boil / toil .

Write the missing numbers.

25 _ _ _ 27   43 _ _ _ 45

39 _ _ _ 41   58 _ _ _ 60

68 _ _ _ 70   49 _ _ _ 51

97 _ _ _ 99   32 _ _ _ 34

READING OUTPOST

Color the sets of rhyming words.

tool — purple
book — yellow
noon — red
zoom — blue

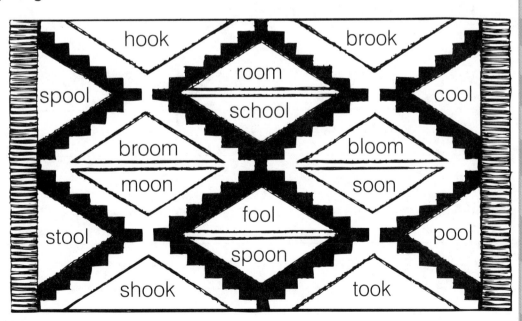

hook   brook
room
spool   cool
school
broom   bloom
moon   soon
fool
stool   pool
spoon
shook   took

Texas Longhorns

How do you think Texas Longhorn cattle got their name? Their long horns make them easy to spot. Some Longhorns have straight horns. Others have horns that twist or curl. Some Longhorns have horns eight feet long!

Most Longhorns are found in the West. Cattle with long horns need good food. Longhorns eat well on grasses growing on the plains of the West.

Answer the questions.

1. How did the Texas Longhorn get its name?

   _____

   _ _ _ _ _ _ _ _ _ _ _ _ _ _ _ _ _ _

   _____

2. How long can their horns get? _____

   _ _ _ _ _ _ _ _ _ _ _ _

3. Why is the West a good place for Longhorns to live?

   _____

   _

   _____

4. Why would a Texas Longhorn not make a good pet?

   _____

   _

   _____

   _____

   _

   _____

Put an X on the coins needed to pay for the item.

penny = _____ ¢   nickel = _____ ¢   dime = _____ ¢   quarter = _____ ¢

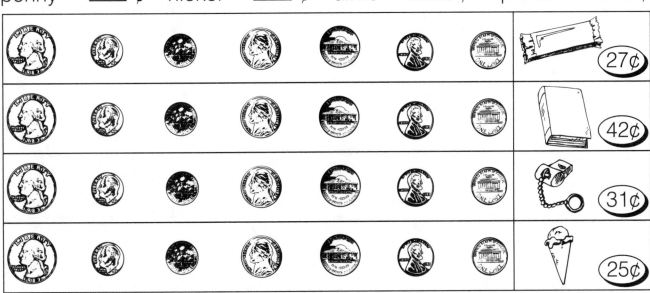

Word Wayside

Circle the correct word.

	The dog is bigger / biggest .
	The turtle is slower / slowest .
	The barn is larger / largest .
	The tree is taller / tallest .

Math Beacon

Circle one-half of the set.

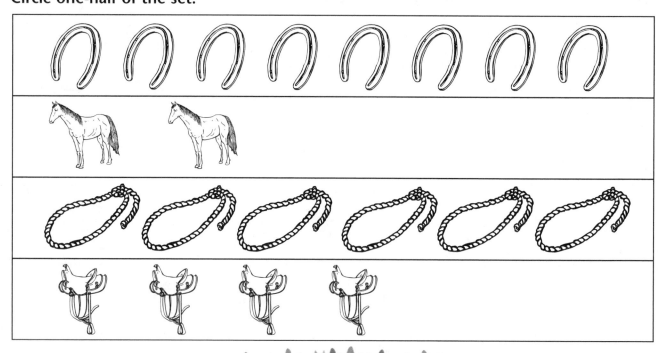

READING OUTPOST

Circle the correct word for each sentence.

1. Each day I do my   chores   chairs .

2. How far can Tim   know   throw   the ball?

3. The children enjoy hearing a good   store   story .

4. I took my dog to Grandmother's   house   horse .

5. Adam   tore   store   his new pants on the fence.

6. Jess will   know   show   Dan his pet turtle.

DAY 3

Write a number sentence for each word problem.

1. Joyce has 10 marbles.
   Dana has 4 marbles.
   How many more marbles does Joyce have?

   _____   _____   _____
   _ _ _ — _ _ _ = _ _ _
   _____   _____   _____   marbles

2. Mike had 12 toy cars.
   He gives 5 cars to Sam.
   How many toy cars does Mike have left?

   _____   _____   _____
   _ _ _ — _ _ _ = _ _ _
   _____   _____   _____   toy cars

Word Wayside

For each c, write s if it has a sound like *ice* and k if it has a sound like *Kate*.

camp   _____

cake   _____

fence   _____

cat   _____

lacy   _____

nice   _____

cute   _____

cowboy   _____

cent   _____

cot   _____

code   _____

candy   _____

Read the sentence.
Circle the correct answer.

1. Tim goes to the lake to fish.

   What does Tim do at the lake?

2. Running Deer rides his pony home.

   Where does Running Deer ride his pony?

3. Mother read the story to me.

   What did Mother read to me?

4. The horse runs up the hill.

   What does the horse run up?

STUDY SKILL
HEADQUARTERS

Write each word under the correct heading.

| Friday | December | Monday |
| August | Wednesday | February |

Days	Draw a picture of something you do in the summer.	Months

Match the picture with the correct temperature.

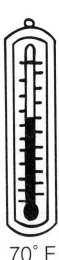

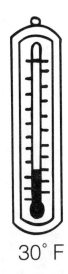

90° F   70° F   30° F

Writer's Nook

Finish writing the story.

Allen found a locked trunk in _____

_____

_____

_____

_____

_____

_____

_____

Solve using the place-value frame.

Tens	Ones
7	9
− 1	1

Tens	Ones
6	7
− 1	3

Tens	Ones
3	5
− 2	3

Tens	Ones
5	8
− 0	3

Tens	Ones
9	9
− 3	3

Tens	Ones
8	2
− 5	0

LANGUAGE LODGE

Read the sentence.
Write the correct word in the blank.

milk	feet	beach	summer	cat

1. <u>Star</u> is to <u>sky</u> as <u>shell</u> is to _____.

2. <u>Eat</u> is to <u>pie</u> as <u>drink</u> is to _____.

3. <u>Puppy</u> is to <u>kitten</u> as <u>dog</u> is to _____.

4. <u>Clap</u> is to <u>hands</u> as <u>stomp</u> is to _____.

5. <u>January</u> is to <u>winter</u> as <u>July</u> is to _____.

Draw a picture of the sentence.

The puppy has a bone.

Fact Harbor

Complete each family of facts.

| 9 | + | 8 | = | 17 |

Find the hidden objects.

horseshoe   horse's head   Indian headdress
cowboy hat   saddle
spur   branding iron

PROGRESS
Week Four

PAGES Circle a for every page completed.

Parent's Initials

DAY 1 •

DAY 2 •

DAY 3 •

DAY 4 •

DAY 5 •

READING Color a for every 10 minutes of reading you do.

DAY 1	DAY 2	DAY 3	DAY 4	DAY 5
☆	☆	☆	☆	☆
☆	☆	☆	☆	☆
☆	☆	☆	☆	☆

Fact Harbor

Color the facts that equal the number in the center.

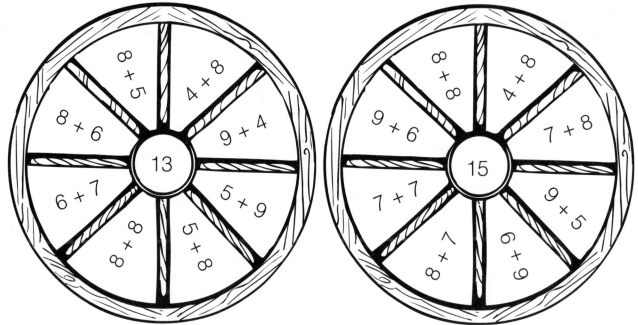

Word Wayside

Circle the correct sound for each picture.

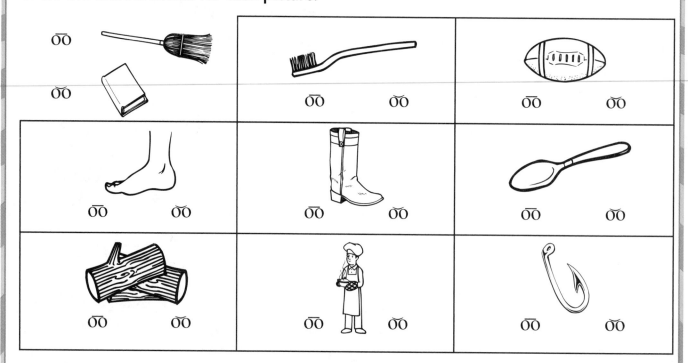

DAY 1

MATH
JUNCTION

Write the number of tens and ones.
Write the number.

| 1 | ten | 5 | ones | 15 |

| | ten | | ones | |

| | ten | | ones | |

| | ten | | ones | |

READING OUTPOST

Draw a line from the picture to the correct word.

thread
bread
head

beet
meet
sheet

beat
heat
seat

seed
need
bleed

Red Moon's Wish

Red Moon saw the horses line up. His father, Three Moons, was the chief. He rode at the front. Red Moon could see his brother in line too. All the men had bows and arrows.

"I wish I could go on the hunt," said Red Moon. "I could kill a deer."

"But I need you here, my son," said his mother. "You must be brave for me. Maybe you can go next year."

Answer the questions.

1. Who is the chief? _____

_____

2. What do all the men have? _____

_____

3. Why do the men need bows and arrows?

_____

_____

4. Why can Red Moon not go on the hunt?

_____

_____

5. When can Red Moon go hunting?

_____

_____

• • • • DAY 2 • • • •

Write the days of the week in order.

Saturday	Wednesday	Monday	Thursday
Tuesday	Friday	Sunday	

1. _____

2. _____

3. _____

4. _____

5. _____

6. _____

7. _____

Word Wayside

Draw lines to form compound words.

barn

sun

home

cup

drug

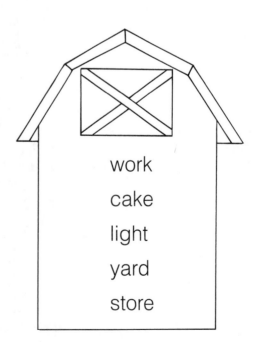

work

cake

light

yard

store

Math Beacon

What comes next? Complete the pattern.

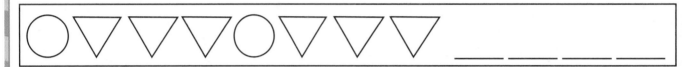

READING OUTPOST

Write the letter of the synonym (word that means the same) of each word.

___ pan   a. story

___ quick   b. grin

___ tore   c. fast

___ tale   d. begin

___ smile   e. pot

___ start   f. ripped

Solve the facts.

10 − 2 = ☐   6 − 6 = ☐   7 − 1 = ☐

11 − 7 = ☐   15 − 8 = ☐   13 − 9 = ☐

12 − 3 = ☐   14 − 5 = ☐   5 − 3 = ☐

4 − 3 = ☐   16 − 8 = ☐   11 − 4 = ☐

Word Wayside

Circle the silent letter(s) in each word.

sight   wrist   sign

knob

lamb   crumb

light

wrench

wrap

READING OUTPOST

Read the sentences. Circle the correct answers.

1. Mary won the race.

   Mary is   fast   slow .

2. Susan helped Tom ride a bike.

   Susan was   kind   unkind .

3. Andy shared his Bible with his friend.

   Andy is   selfish   unselfish .

4. Alan jumped up and down with joy.

   Alan was   happy   sad .

STUDY SKILL
◆ HEADQUARTERS ◆

Use the map to fill in the blanks.

How many

_____ churches

_____ schools

_____ trees

_____ houses

_____ stores

are there in the town?

MAP KEY

🏠 house   🏪 store

⛪ church   🏫 school   🌳 tree

DAY 4

Start at the ●. Count the objects around each picture. Write your answer in the box.

Writer's Nook

Finish writing the story.

If I were hiking and saw a snake, I would

Math Beacon

Color.

circle – yellow
square – blue
rectangle – green
triangle – orange

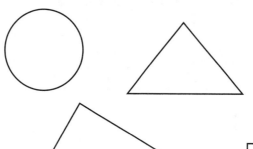
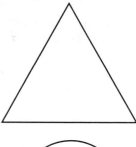

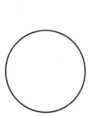

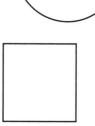

LANGUAGE LODGE

Add the correct punctuation (. or ?) to each sentence.

1. My Bible is on the table

2. Who made the cookies for the party

3. The horse ran fast up the hill

4. How high can you jump

5. Who made you

6. God made me and all things

7. Where is the ball for the game

8. We need another girl for our team

DAY 5

Draw a picture of the sentence.

A big frog is on the log.

Fact Harbor

**Write an equation for each word problem.
Solve it.**

Seth baked 7 muffins.
Anna baked 6 muffins.
How many did they bake together?

| 7 | + | 6 | = | | muffins

Ben ate 3 eggs.
Beth ate 2 eggs.
How many eggs did they both eat?

| | | | | | eggs

Color by number.

1. green
2. gray
3. brown
4. blue

5. purple
6. light green
7. black
8. red

PROGRESS

Week Five

 PAGES Circle a for every page completed.

Parent's Initials

DAY 1 •

DAY 2 •

DAY 3 •

DAY 4 •

DAY 5 •

READING Color a for every 10 minutes of reading you do.

DAY 1	DAY 2	DAY 3	DAY 4	DAY 5
☆	☆	☆	☆	☆
☆	☆	☆	☆	☆
☆	☆	☆	☆	☆

49

 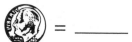 

Math Beacon

Write the value of each coin.

 = _____   = _____   = _____   = _____

Put an *X* on the coins that equal a quarter.

Word Wayside

Circle the correct word.

baseball
ballpark

fawn
paw

jaw
crawl

paw
straw

baseball
football

claw
law

lawn
yawn

hawk
jaw

DAY 1

MATH JUNCTION

Count by 2s.
Write the missing numbers.

2	4		8	
		16		
22		26	28	
32	34			
	44		48	

READING OUTPOST

Circle the correct answer.

1. I ate a piece of   nudge   fudge .

2. Our teacher led us in the   ledge   pledge   to the flag.

3. The creek ran under the   ridge   bridge .

4. The cook gave me a   pledge   wedge   of pie.

5. The   judge   fudge   said the man disobeyed.

6. The frog sat on the lily pad and did not   budge   judge .

HELP NEEDED FOR CATTLE DRIVE

Are you a cowboy who is out of work? Do you have good horses? Can you ride well? Would you like to work on a cattle drive next week?

The Lazy R Ranch needs five more cowboys with good horses to help drive a herd to Fort Worth, Texas. Ride out to the Lazy R Ranch tomorrow to meet the trail boss and to sign up. The trail boss will pay you when the job is done.

Circle the correct answer.

1. Only two more cowboys are needed for the cattle drive.   true, false

2. The cowboys must have good horses.
   true, false

3. The trail boss will pay the cowboys when the job is done.   true, false

Write your answer.

4. Why would you like to be a cowboy at the

   _____

Lazy R Ranch? _____

   _____

   _____

   _____

MATH JUNCTION

Write an equation for each word problem. Solve it.

1. There are 7 balls in the box.
   Trent adds 2 more balls.
   How many balls are there in all?

   _7_ + _2_ = _9_ balls

2. Sandy has 5 yellow flowers.
   She cut 4 more flowers.
   How many flowers does Sandy have in all?

   _ _ _ + _ _ _ = _ _ _ flowers

Word Wayside

Add *s* or *es* to the words. Remember to add *es* after *ch*, *sh*, *s*, and *z*.

pass _____

rope _____

coach _____

horse _____

rider _____

cowboy _____

catch _____

desert _____

dish _____

buzz _____

Math Beacon

Circle the objects that have been divided in equal parts.

READING OUTPOST

Write an antonym (opposite) for each word.

| well | sister | fat | stop | sit | glad | light | old |

go _____   sick _____

young _____   stand _____

dark _____   brother _____

sad _____   slim _____

DAY 3

Solve the facts.

3	7	7	8	5
− 2	− 5	− 6	− 2	− 5

5	6	9	4	10
− 4	− 5	− 7	− 3	− 4

Word Wayside

Circle the correct beginning or ending sound.

 c ck	 c ck	 c ck
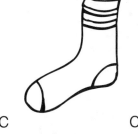 c ck	 c ck	 c ck

Read the sentences.
Circle the correct answer in each sentence.

1. Jim and Joe are on the baseball team.
   Who is on the baseball team?
2. The mittens are on the table.
   What is on the table?
3. The cactus out west grows tall.
   What grows tall out west?
4. The cowboys take care of the cattle.
   Who takes care of the cattle?
5. The branding iron was in the barn.
   What was in the barn?

STUDY SKILL
◆ HEADQUARTERS ◆

Write each group of letters in alphabetical order.

q o p   f d e   l m k

c b a   t u s

a b c d e f g h i j k l m n o p q r s t u v w x y z

DAY 4

Math Beacon

Write the number of centimeters.

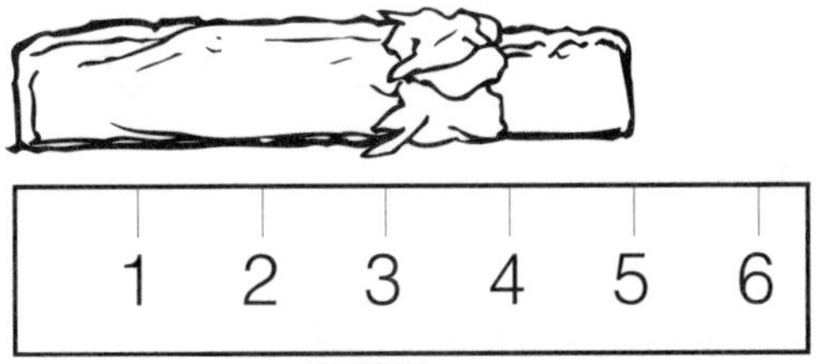

☐ cm

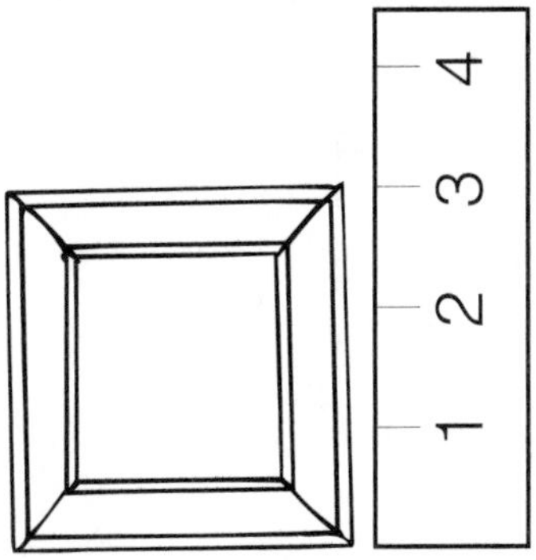

☐ cm

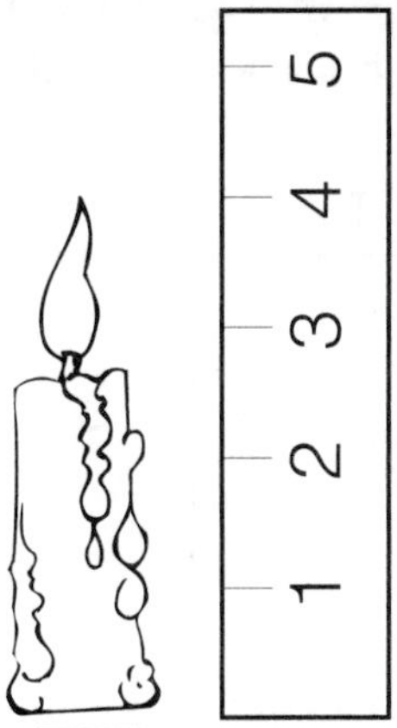

☐ cm

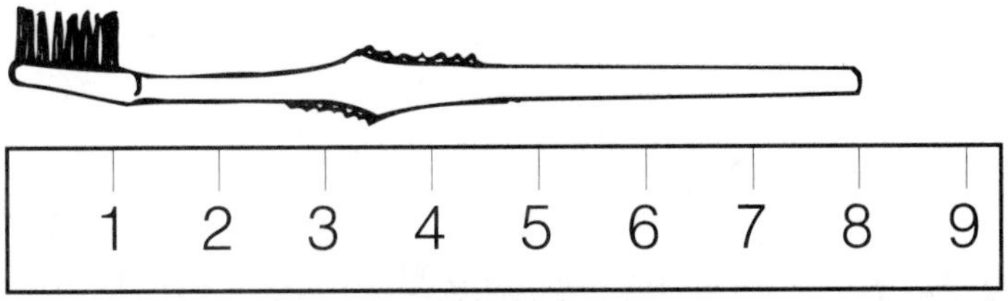

☐ cm

Writer's Nook

Finish writing the story.

If I were a stagecoach driver, I would ______________________

____

____

____

____

Solve each problem using the place-value frame.

Tens	Ones
1	5
+ 2	3

Tens	Ones
2	1
+ 3	8

Tens	Ones
3	5
+ 6	0

Tens	Ones
4	6
+ 3	3

Tens	Ones
7	0
+ 2	0

Tens	Ones
8	8
+ 1	1

Tens	Ones
6	2
+ 0	7

Tens	Ones
3	2
+ 5	6

LANGUAGE LODGE

Use words from the boxes to complete these compound words.

| lace   hive   day   drop   ball |

rain _____

shoe _____

birth _____

meat _____

bee _____

| flake   trap   shore   box   town |

mail _____

sea _____

mouse _____

down _____

snow _____

DAY 5

Draw a picture of the sentence.

The wagon wheel rolled down the hill.

Fact Harbor

Complete each family of facts.

4	+	5	=	9

Decorate and color each thumbprint.

··PROGRESS··

Week Six

PAGES — Circle a  for every page completed.

Parent's Initials

DAY 1 •

DAY 2 •

DAY 3 •

DAY 4 •

DAY 5 •

READING — Color a ☆ for every 10 minutes of reading you do.

DAY 1	DAY 2	DAY 3	DAY 4	DAY 5
☆	☆	☆	☆	☆
☆	☆	☆	☆	☆
☆	☆	☆	☆	☆

Fact Harbor

Color the correct oval.

9	7	5	9	7	4
+ 9	+ 7	+ 5	+ 8	+ 5	+ 7
○ 17	○ 14	○ 10	○ 17	○ 13	○ 11
○ 18	○ 13	○ 11	○ 16	○ 12	○ 12

8	6	4	8	5	3
+ 8	+ 6	+ 4	+ 6	+ 8	+ 8
○ 16	○ 11	○ 7	○ 15	○ 13	○ 10
○ 15	○ 12	○ 8	○ 14	○ 14	○ 11

Word Wayside

Circle the correct word.

due
true
glue

screw
few
dew

clue
Sue
blue

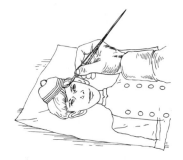

new
grew
drew

MATH JUNCTION

Write the tens and ones.

35 = __3__ tens __5__ ones   99 = ____ tens ____ ones

51 = ____ tens ____ ones   79 = ____ tens ____ ones

55 = ____ tens ____ ones   86 = ____ tens ____ ones

37 = ____ tens ____ ones   48 = ____ tens ____ ones

18 = ____ tens ____ ones   14 = ____ tens ____ ones

60 = ____ tens ____ ones   28 = ____ tens ____ ones

READING OUTPOST

Add a word to each word family.

_____

ox

_____

wax

_____

box

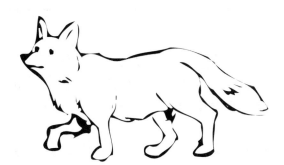

_____

tax

A Plant that Heals

The cactus is a desert plant. Most cactus plants are light green or yellow. They can be short and round like balls. Or they can be tall with thin arms. Some have pretty flowers. But don't try to pick one! Cactus plants also have prickly spines that can stick you.

Many kinds of cactus plants can be used for healing. Inside the prickly pear cactus is a sap. This sap can help to heal sunburn or snakebite. Some cactus plants can help treat pain. But first you have to take their spines off!

Write the answers.

1. What color are cactus plants?

   _____

   _

   _____

2. Why should you not pick a cactus plant?

   _____

   _

   _____

3. What can the cactus sap be used for?

   _____

   _

   _____

4. How could you get the spines off of a cactus plant?

   _____

   _

   _____

Write the hour.
Count by 5s and write the minutes.

Word Wayside

Clap the syllables.
Circle the correct number of horseshoes.

dishes

printed

buzz

backpack

cobweb

fish

hunted

upset

passes

horse

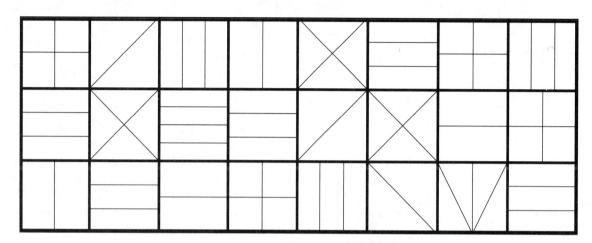

Math Beacon

Color the blocks according to the key.

halves 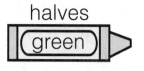 green

thirds 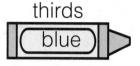 blue

fourths 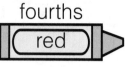 red

READING OUTPOST

Circle the correct action word.

1. The prairie dog tampered / scampered into a hole.

2. The horses trotted / rotted down the path.

3. The cactus knows / grows everywhere out west.

4. The cowboy battled / saddled his horse.

5. The cowboy pitched / ditched his tent for the night.

•••• DAY 3 ••••

Solve the facts.

11 − 5	12 − 7	12 − 3	9 − 1
17 − 9	5 − 4	10 − 2	7 − 6
10 − 3	6 − 2	7 − 1	13 − 6

Word Wayside

Circle the beginning or ending *th*.

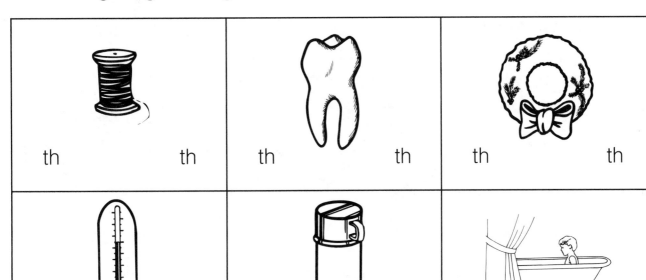

| th   th | th   th | th   th |
| th   th | th   th | th   th |

Read the sentences.
Draw a line from each picture to the correct sentence.

> The cowboy roped the bull.
> The cowboy roped the horse.

> The bug crawled on the ground.
> The bug crawled on the leaf.

> The toy dog is on wheels.
> The toy dog is under the bed.

STUDY SKILL
HEADQUARTERS

Follow the directions.

1. Put a bell on the bull's neck.
2. Draw grass under the bull's feet.
3. Put a sun in the sky.
4. Color the bull.

DAY 4

Fill in the correct oval.

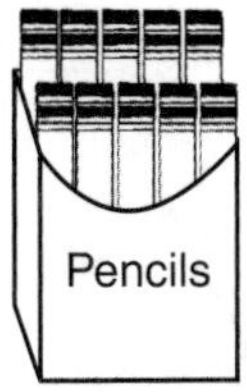 Pencils ○ more ○ less than one pound	 ○ more ○ less than one pound
 Sugar ○ more ○ less than one pound	 ○ more ○ less than one pound

Writer's Nook

Finish writing the story.

You begin to look for some wood for a campfire. _____

Suddenly you see a _____

_____

_____

_____

_____

_____

_____

_____

Math Beacon

What comes next?

e   f   e   f   e   f   _____ _____

▽ ○ ▽ ○ ▽ ○ ▽ _____ _____

◇ 8 ◇ 8 ◇ 8 ◇ 8 _____ _____

□ □ ○ □ □ ○ _____ _____

○ △ □ ○ △ □ _____ _____

LANGUAGE LODGE

Choose the best describing word for the underlined word.

honest	stronger	scared	big

_____

1. The <u>bison</u> is a _____ animal.

_____

2. The _____ <u>prairie</u> <u>dog</u> ran quickly into his hole.

_____

3. <u>Rick</u> was _____ when he returned the wallet.

_____

4. <u>Bill</u> is _____ than Caleb.

···· DAY 5 ····

Draw a picture of the sentence.

The puppy is wearing a hat.

MATH JUNCTION

Write a number sentence for each word problem.

1. Ted dug up 12 worms.
   He lost 4 worms.
   How many worms does he have left?

   _____ _____ _____
   _ _ _ _ _ _ _ = _ _ _
   _____ _____ _____ worms

2. Deb had 9 goldfish.
   She gave Sarah 4.
   How many goldfish does she have now?

   _____ _____ _____
   _ _ _ _ _ _ _ = _ _ _
   _____ _____ _____ goldfish

Look at the pictures.
Circle what is missing.
Draw the missing item in the picture.
You may color the pictures.

horseshoes

mane

saddle

belt

hat

boot

grass

wheel

hay

··PROGRESS··

Week Seven

PAGES ▸ Circle a 👢 for every page completed.

Parent's Initials

DAY 1 • 👢 👢

DAY 2 • 👢 👢

DAY 3 • 👢 👢

DAY 4 • 👢 👢

DAY 5 • 👢 👢

READING ▸ Color a ☆ for every 10 minutes of reading you do.

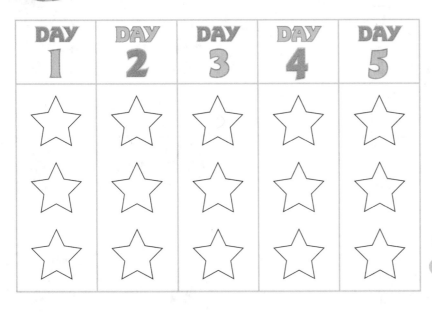

DAY 1	DAY 2	DAY 3	DAY 4	DAY 5
☆	☆	☆	☆	☆
☆	☆	☆	☆	☆
☆	☆	☆	☆	☆

73

Fact Harbor

Follow the directions to solve the facts.

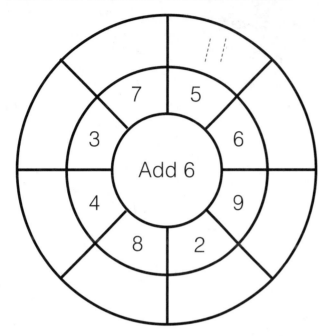
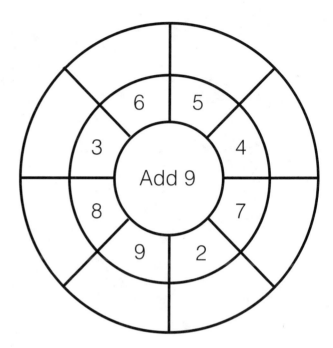

Word Wayside

Color the cow that shows the sound that *y* makes in each word.

fly

penny

rainy

funny

dry

fry

DAY 1

Count from 1 to 50.
Write the missing numbers.

1	2			5			8		
		13			16			19	
			24			27			
31	32			35			38		
		43			46				

READING OUTPOST

Read each word family. Draw a line from each picture to the
correct word.

lube
tube
cube

flute
mute
cute

June
prune
tune

Driving a Stagecoach

1. Do you think you would like to drive a stagecoach? Coach drivers had a hard job. They had to know all about horses. They drove in the ice and snow. Sometimes they had to drive in the dark.

2. Each driver would cover one part of the trail. He needed to know the roads well. Sometimes the roads went up the sides of the hills. Sometimes the roads went along cliffs. The driver had a risky job.

Read the story.
Write the number of the paragraph above that gives the information.

☐ Sometimes the roads went along cliffs.

☐ The driver had a risky job.

☐ Coach drivers had a hard job.

☐ Drivers needed to know the roads well.

☐ Sometimes they had to drive in the dark.

☐ They drove in ice and snow.

Tell why you would like to drive a stagecoach.

_____

_____

_____

_____

Put an _X_ on the coins needed.

🪙🪙🪙🪙🪙🪙🪙	🍇 71¢
🪙🪙🪙🪙🪙🪙🪙	🍎🍎 48¢
🪙🪙🪙🪙🪙🪙🪙	🍌 34¢
🪙🪙🪙🪙🪙🪙	🍊 60¢

Word Wayside

Circle the correct word.

1. Hannah was the   fastest   faster   runner of all the girls.

2. Mary jumped rope   longer   longest   than Diane.

3. Ellen had the   newest   newer   bookbag of all the boys
   and girls in the class.

4. The turtle is   slowest   slower   than the rabbit.

5. That cowboy is the   taller   tallest   of all the men.

Math Beacon

Color the hats according to the key.

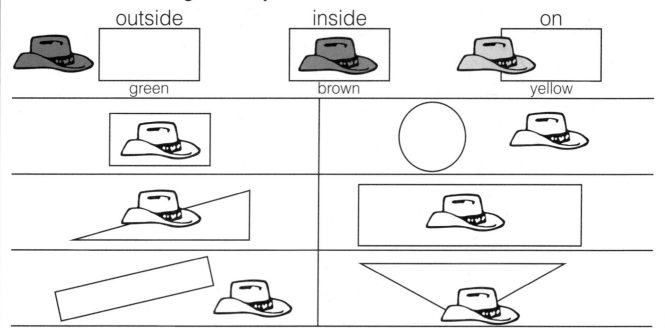

outside — green
inside — brown
on — yellow

READING OUTPOST

Read the words on the signs. Color each pair of synonyms (words that mean the same) the same color.

Write an equation for each word problem.
Solve it.

Robert has 7 tents.
Ed has 3 tents.
How many more tents does Robert have than Ed?

    tents

Roger has 6 horseshoes.
Greg has 4 horseshoes.
How many horseshoes do they have altogether?

   horseshoes

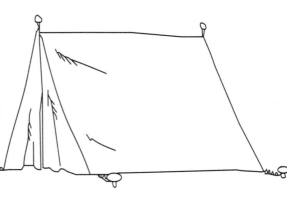

Word Wayside

Draw a line from the picture to the correct sentence.

Spray the water.
Spring the water.

Meg strikes the tub.
Meg scrubs the tub.

The kite string broke.
The kite stray broke.

The cowboy strums the song.
The cowboy straps the song.

Read each sentence and question. Circle the correct answer.

1. The baby can crawl.
   What can the baby do?

2. The horse has a saddle on its back.
   What does the horse have on its back?

3. Clouds are in the sky.
   What are in the sky?

4. The horse ran into the hills.
   What ran into the hills?

5. The grass in the field is turning green.
   What is turning green?

STUDY SKILL
HEADQUARTERS

Use the items from the pencil to fill in the lists.

Things to Do

_____
__ __ __ __ __ __ __
_____
__ __ __ __ __ __ __
_____
__ __ __ __ __ __ __
_____

sit
pan
shout
pencil
sing
broom
talk
stove

Things to Use

_____
__ __ __ __ __ __ __
_____
__ __ __ __ __ __ __
_____

Circle the longest object.
Put an X on the shortest object.

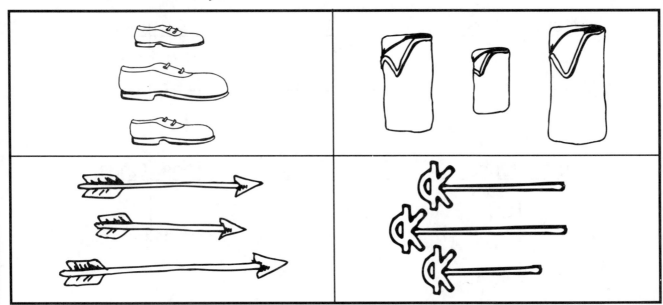

Writer's Nook

Finish writing the story.

My dad and I are hiking in the woods. _____

_ _

I smell smoke. I _____

_____

_ _

_____

_____

_ _

_____

_ _

_____

MATH
JUNCTION

Solve each problem using the place-value frame.

Tens	Ones
4	7
− 1	7

Tens	Ones
8	8
− 4	7

Tens	Ones
3	7
− 2	5

Tens	Ones
7	2
− 5	1

Tens	Ones
9	1
− 8	0

Tens	Ones
2	3
− 1	3

LANGUAGE LODGE

Put *F* if the sentence is fanciful.
Put *T* if the sentence could be true.

_____ 1. The prairie dogs talked about the hawk.

_____ 2. The horse galloped down the trail.

_____ 3. Billy Bookworm ate part of the book.

_____ 4. The cow jumped over the moon.

_____ 5. All our family will go to the park.

_____ 6. The elephant sprayed water on me.

DAY 5

Draw a picture of the sentence.

The cowboy feeds the cattle.

Fact Harbor

Complete each family of facts.

9	+	4	=	13

STATION BREAK

Circle the things wrong in the picture.

··P R O G R E S S··

Week Eight

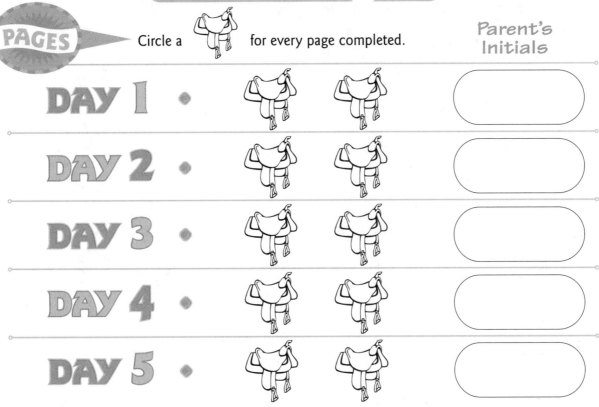

PAGES ▸ Circle a 🐴 for every page completed.

Parent's Initials

DAY 1 ·

DAY 2 ·

DAY 3 ·

DAY 4 ·

DAY 5 ·

READING ▸ Color a ☆ for every 10 minutes of reading you do.

DAY 1	DAY 2	DAY 3	DAY 4	DAY 5
☆	☆	☆	☆	☆
☆	☆	☆	☆	☆
☆	☆	☆	☆	☆

Write an equation for each word problem. Solve.

Carl has 4 sacks of grain. Dan has 5 sacks of grain. Randy has 6 sacks of grain. How many sacks are there?

☐ ☐ ☐ ☐ ☐ ☐ ☐ sacks

Kristy wants 2 hamburgers. Jason wants 2 hamburgers. Uncle Will wants 3 hamburgers. How many hamburgers need to be made?

☐ ☐ ☐ ☐ ☐ ☐ ☐ hamburgers

Word Wayside

Write the vowel sound you hear in each picture.

| ā | ē | ī | ō | ū |

_____

_ _ _

_____

_____

_ _ _

_____

_____

_ _ _

_____

_____

_ _ _

_____

Circle the correct number in each set.

$\dfrac{1}{\text{half}}$				
$\dfrac{1}{\text{fourth}}$				
$\dfrac{1}{\text{third}}$				
$\dfrac{1}{\text{fourth}}$				
$\dfrac{1}{\text{half}}$				

READING OUTPOST

Read each word family.
Draw a line from the picture to the correct word.

bite

kite

white

flight

sight

bright

might

right

light

write

bite

quite

DAY 1

The American Bison

The bison is one of the biggest animals in the West. It has a huge head with horns. It also has a large hump on its back. Most bison are dark brown or black.

Bison live in herds. They feed on the grass of the plains. They also eat small shrubs.

Long ago, Native Americans hunted bison. They ate bison meat. They also made shoes from its hide. They used its horns to make arrows. Today most bison live on the plains of the West. You might also see them at the zoo.

Write the answers.

1. The bison has a huge head with _____.

2. What color are most bison? _____

3. What did Native Americans use bison for? _____

4. Where do most bison live today? _____

5. Why is the West a good place for bison to live? _____

DAY 2

Write the missing months.

November	July	March	January	June	September

	May	
February		*October*
April	*August*	*December*

Word Wayside

Divide each underlined word into syllables.

Example: c l a s s•e s

1. The cowboy is <u>w a l k i n g</u> to his horse.

2. The cactus was <u>t a l l e r</u> than Kevin.

3. The rodeo is <u>s o o n e r</u> than the fair.

4. The deer <u>r e s t e d</u> by the fence.

5. The pines are <u>t a l l e r</u> than the oaks.

6. Linda was <u>r e a d i n g</u> when Mom called her.

M·A·T·H JUNCTION

Complete the number sentence with = or ≠.

70 + 4 ☐ 75

30 + 6 ☐ 39

10 + 8 ☐ 19

50 + 3 ☐ 53

20 + 2 ☐ 21

90 + 3 ☐ 93

60 + 8 ☐ 69

40 + 5 ☐ 45

20 + 7 ☐ 26

90 + 6 ☐ 96

60 + 5 ☐ 64

80 + 4 ☐ 84

30 + 8 ☐ 39

70 + 1 ☐ 71

READING OUTPOST

Write the antonym (opposite) for each word.

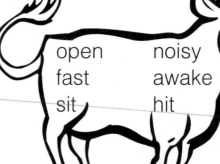

open   noisy
fast   awake
sit   hit

1. miss _____

2. slow _____

3. quiet _____

4. stand _____

5. asleep _____

6. close _____

••••• DAY 3 •••••

Solve each fact.
Color the boxes red that have 8 as the answer.

17 − 8	14 − 7	13 − 5
11 − 6	16 − 8	10 − 8
15 − 7	12 − 8	18 − 9

Draw lines to match the words and the pictures.

telephone

gift

elephant

trophy

roof

hoof

READING OUTPOST

Read the sentences.
Mark the correct answers.

1. Terry mopped up the water for Mother. ○ Terry was helpful. ○ Terry was not helpful.	2. Meg won the sprint. ○ Meg is a fast runner. ○ Meg is a slow runner.
3. Mike thanked the coach for giving him the trophy. ○ Mike was selfish. ○ Mike was thankful.	4. Mark planted flowers for Mrs. Tomkins. ○ Mark was kind. ○ Mark was angry.

STUDY SKILL
◆ HEADQUARTERS ◆

Use the map to complete each sentence.

Mary's house

Elm St.

The school is on _____.

The church is on _____.

Willow St.

Oak St.

Maple St.

Ed's Foods

FIREHOUSE

Mary lives on _____.

The fire station is on _____.

Pine St.

SCHOOL

The grocery store is on _____.

•••• DAY 4 ••••

Circle which holds more.

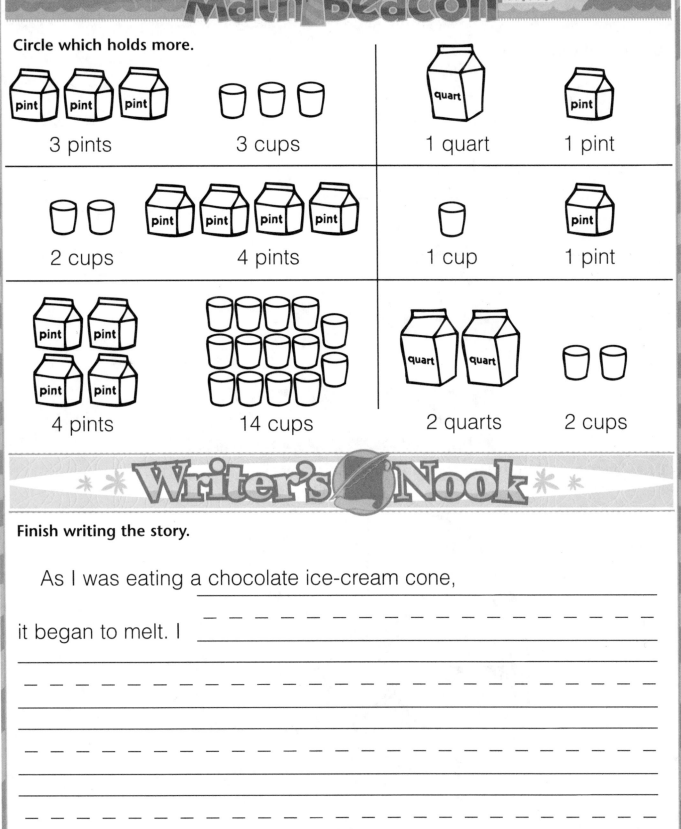

3 pints   3 cups

1 quart   1 pint

2 cups   4 pints

1 cup   1 pint

4 pints   14 cups

2 quarts   2 cups

Finish writing the story.

As I was eating a chocolate ice-cream cone, _____

it began to melt. I _____

_____

_____

_____

_____

_____

Math Beacon

Draw what comes next.

_____ _____

_____ _____

_____ _____

_____ _____

LANGUAGE LODGE

Draw lines to match the contractions with the correct words.

let's   don't

I'm   it's

can't   won't

I'll   doesn't

I am   it is
let us   do not
cannot   will not
I will   does not

Draw a picture of the sentence.

The rattlesnake crawled in the weeds.

Fact Harbor

Complete each family of facts.

14		7	
9	5	2	5

9	+	5	=	14

Read each clue.
Find the words that tell you about a cowboy and his horse.

Down
1. what you can put a saddle on
2. what a horse wears on its feet
3. what you put on a horse's back

Across
4. a rope
5. wheels attached to the heels of a rider's boots
6. the long hair on a horse's neck

lasso

horse

spurs

shoes

saddle

mane

··◆ P R O G R E S S ◆··
Week Nine

PAGES ▶ Circle a for every page completed.

Parent's Initials

DAY 1 •

DAY 2 •

DAY 3 •

DAY 4 •

DAY 5 •

READING ▶ Color a for every 10 minutes of reading you do.

DAY 1	DAY 2	DAY 3	DAY 4	DAY 5
☆	☆	☆	☆	☆
☆	☆	☆	☆	☆
☆	☆	☆	☆	☆

Fact Harbor

Solve the facts.

2 + 7	2 + 9
3 + 8	3 + 4
5 + 6	5 + 0

6 + 5	6 + 3
4 + 4	4 + 2
8 + 9	8 + 8

Word Wayside

Color the oval by each word that has a long vowel sound.

- ◯ sky
- ◯ tell
- ◯ trick
- ◯ me
- ◯ she
- ◯ fly

- ◯ he
- ◯ dry
- ◯ chug
- ◯ lump
- ◯ my
- ◯ be

DAY 1

Write the number of tens and ones.

20 _2_ tens _0_ ones   68 ____ tens ____ ones

39 ____ tens ____ ones   72 ____ tens ____ ones

93 ____ tens ____ ones   47 ____ tens ____ ones

51 ____ tens ____ ones   19 ____ tens ____ ones

85 ____ tens ____ ones   89 ____ tens ____ ones

READING OUTPOST

Put an *X* on the word that does not belong in the word family.

night
day
fight

nigh
high
neck

light
strong
might

tight
left
right

sight
flight
sky

sail
sigh

The Sod House

Jenny stood by the door of the sod house. She looked up at the sky. Black clouds were rolling in from the west. A raindrop fell on her nose. Jenny went back inside. "Papa, will we be safe?"

Papa pulled the door shut. "The roof is sound," he said. "The walls are strong. We will be safe in our sod house. God brought us here to Nebraska. He will take care of us."

Read the story.
Circle the correct answers.

1. The house is made of   sod   soap .

2. The day is   sunny   cloudy .

3. The walls are   wrong   strong .

4. Papa and Jenny   are   are not   safe in the house.

5. God   will   will not   take care of Papa and Jenny.

How does God take care of you?

_____

_____

_____

_____

_____

DAY 2

Write an equation for each word problem.
Solve it.

Tasha has 25¢.
Her dad gives her 20¢.
How much money does Tasha have in all?

 ¢

Aunt Ellen gave Tim 32¢.
Uncle Carl gave him 21¢.
How much money does Tim have in all?

 ¢

Word Wayside

Put a letter in each boot and add a suffix.
Draw a line from each picture to the correct word.

bat [ ] ed

skip [ ]

chat [ ]

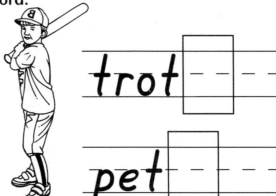

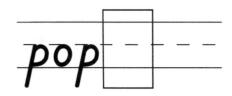

trot [ ]

pet [ ]

pop [ ]

Math Beacon

Divide the shapes into equal parts.

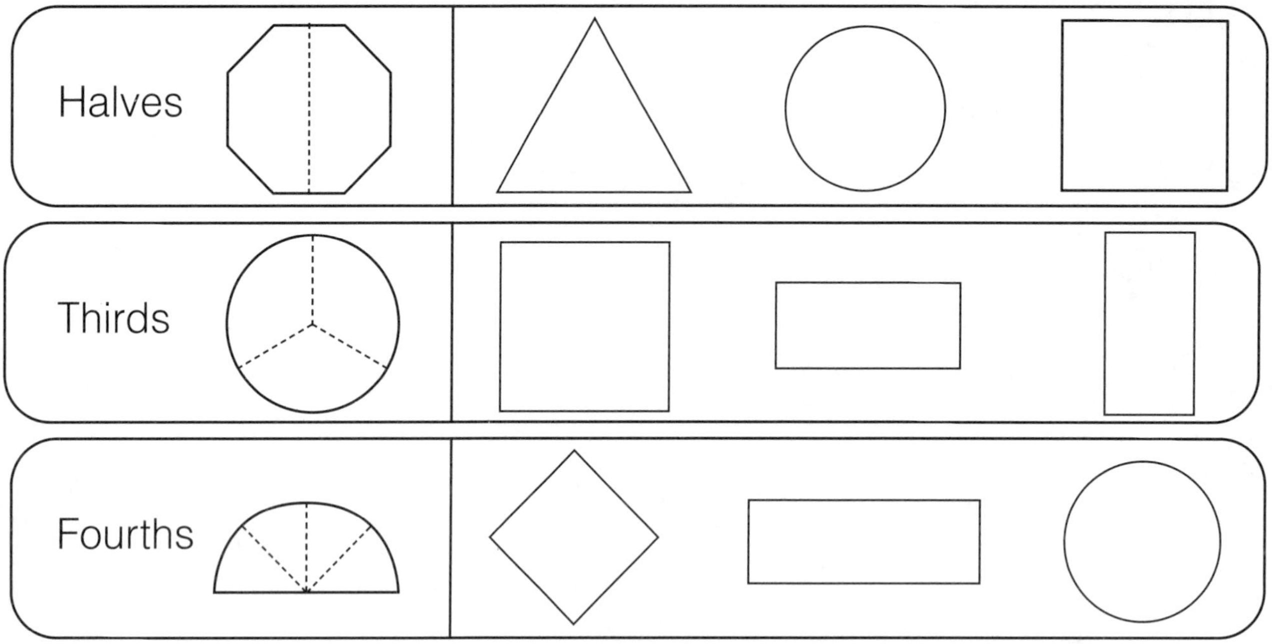

Halves		
Thirds		
Fourths		

READING OUTPOST

Write the correct word.

clock	flute	stuck	time	hill

1. The cowboy _____ a feather in his hat.

2. Nell played her _____ for Lena.

3. What _____ did Dustin arrive at school?

4. The cattle ran up the _____ to the barn.

5. The _____ on the wall had stopped.

••••• DAY 3 •••••

Solve the facts.

$8 - 8 =$

$8 - 3 =$

$8 - 7 =$

$7 - 2 =$

$8 - 1 =$

$8 - 6 =$

$7 - 7 =$

$7 - 5 =$

$7 - 4 =$

$7 - 6 =$

$8 - 4 =$

Word Wayside

Draw a line from each word to the picture with the same *g* sound.

garden   ginger

gentleman   goat

gym   goggles

guard   gem

Draw a line from the picture to the correct sentence.

The girl ran down the stairs.
The girl ran up the stairs.

Many fish are in the pond.
Many fish are in the stream.

The cactus has thorns.
The cactus has flowers.

STUDY SKILL
HEADQUARTERS

Number each set of words in alphabetical order.

a b c d e f g h i j k l m n o p q r s t u v w x y z

____ shape

____ ride

____ no

____ fall

____ dig

____ store

____ bat

____ pull

____ stand

____ my

____ truck

____ come

Put an *X* on the boxes with objects holding less than one liter.
Color the boxes with objects holding more than one liter.

   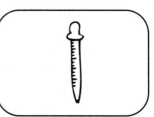

   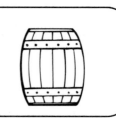

Writer's Nook

Finish writing the story.

It was my first time riding. As soon as I sat in the saddle,

the horse _____

_____

_____

_____

_____

_____

_____

_____

Solve each problem.

```
  4          3          4          5
  3          5          7          4
+ 2        + 7        + 8        + 4
```

LANGUAGE LODGE

Choose a more colorful action verb for the underlined word in the sentence.

> leaps   paddles   frightens   tweets

1. The bird <u>sings</u> in the tree.

   _____

   The bird _____ in the tree.

2. The duck <u>swims</u> around the pond.

   _____

   The duck _____ around the pond.

3. The kangaroo <u>hops</u> across the fields.

   _____

   The kangaroo _____ across the fields.

4. The cat <u>scares</u> the mouse.

   _____

   The cat _____ the mouse.

Draw a picture of the sentence.

The saddle is too big for the pony.

Fact Harbor

Complete each family of facts.

7	+	4	=	11

STATION BREAK

Put an *X* on the picture that is the same as the first picture.

PROGRESS

 Week Ten

Circle a  for every page completed.

Parent's Initials

DAY 1 •

DAY 2 •

DAY 3 •

DAY 4 •

DAY 5 •

READING

Color a for every 10 minutes of reading you do.

DAY 1	DAY 2	DAY 3	DAY 4	DAY 5
☆	☆	☆	☆	☆
☆	☆	☆	☆	☆
☆	☆	☆	☆	☆

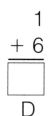

Fact Harbor

Solve the facts to read the message.

$$1 + 6 = \boxed{}$$
D

$$3 + 7 = \boxed{}$$
O

$$3 + 9 = \boxed{}$$
U

$$4 + 2 = \boxed{}$$
V

$$4 + 7 = \boxed{}$$
E

$$7 + 7 = \boxed{}$$
L

$$0 + 8 = \boxed{}$$
Y

$$4 + 9 = \boxed{}$$
S

$$3 + 1 = \boxed{}$$
G

$$\overline{4} \ \overline{10} \ \overline{7} \qquad \overline{14} \ \overline{10} \ \overline{6} \ \overline{11} \ \overline{13} \qquad \overline{8} \ \overline{10} \ \overline{12} \ .$$

Word Wayside

Write the vowel sound you hear in the middle of the words.

a bl__ck m__ne

 a p__n with a l__d

 a p__g in a b__x

 a d__g with a b__ne

DAY 1

MATH JUNCTION

Count by 2s, 5s, and 10s. Write the missing numbers.

54		58			64		68		
74	76			84			90		

5				25				45	
	60			75		85		95	

10			40		60		80		100

READING OUTPOST

Write the correct word.

shield   field   thief   chief   niece   piece

_____   _____   _____

_ _ _ _ _ _ _   _ _ _ _ _ _ _   _ _ _ _ _ _ _

_____   _____   _____

My Pony and Me

We make a fine pair,
My pony and me.
We both wear our hair
Hanging long, loose, and free.

He loves to run,
And I love to ride.
We both think it's fun
To spend all day outside—

To trot up the lane
Past the old tool shed
With the wind in our mane
And the sky straight ahead.

Follow the instructions.

1. Circle the word in the poem that rhymes with *pair*.

2. Why does the rider like to be outside?

   _____

   _ _ _ _ _ _ _ _ _ _ _ _ _ _ _

   _____

   _____

   _ _ _ _ _ _ _ _ _ _ _ _ _ _ _

   _____

3. Where could you ride your pony?

   _____

   _ _ _ _ _ _ _ _ _ _ _ _ _ _ _

   _____

   _____

   _ _ _ _ _ _ _ _ _ _ _ _ _ _ _

   _____

   _ _ _ _ _ _ _ _ _ _ _ _ _ _ _

   _____

In the box above, draw a picture
of yourself riding a pony.

••••• DAY 2 •••••

Circle the correct time.

4:15   12:40   6:30   2:25

5:15   1:40   6:00   3:25

Word Wayside

Color the oval that shows the correct syllables.

◯ litt●le
◯ lit●tle

◯ pret●ty
◯ prett●y

◯ big●ger
◯ bi●gger

◯ let●ter
◯ lett●er

◯ fit●ted
◯ fitt●ed

◯ ha●ppy
◯ hap●py

◯ su●nny
◯ sun●ny

Math Beacon

Write the fraction for the colored part.

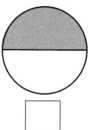

☐

half

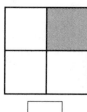

☐

fourth

☐

third

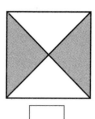

☐

fourths

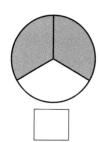

☐

thirds

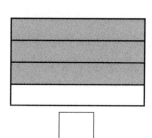

☐

fourths

READING OUTPOST

Draw a line to match the synonyms (words that mean the same).

small	look		stage	same
begin	start		trip	platform
sick	rest		alike	stair
see	little		below	stumble
sleep	ill		step	underneath

DAY 3

Fact Harbor

Solve the facts.

15 − 9	14 − 7	15 − 7	15 − 6

14 − 6	14 − 8	14 − 9

16 − 8	16 − 9	16 − 7	15 − 8

Word Wayside

Add the correct blend to name the picture.

gr   pr   tr

_____ain    _____apes

_____ize   _____ee

_____andfather    _____ince

READING OUTPOST

Read the sentences. Circle the answer.

1. Mark will sit on the grass.
   Who will sit on the grass?

2. Nicky and Robin will read their books.
   What will Robin and Nicky read?

3. Beth played in the rain last Saturday.
   What did Beth play in last Saturday?

4. Dad bought the horse for Justin and Jill.
   What did Dad buy for Justin and Jill?

5. Mandy drank milk with her piece of cake.
   What did Mandy drink with her piece of cake?

STUDY SKILL
❖ HEADQUARTERS ❖

Follow the directions to decorate the belt.

1. Put a yellow O on the belt.
2. Next put a red **+** on the belt.
3. Then put an orange **S** on the belt.
4. Put a blue X on the belt.
5. Next put a green ☐ on the belt.

Write the number of inches.

1   2   3   ☐ inch(es)

1   2   3   ☐ inch(es)

3   2   1   ☐ inch(es)

Finish writing the story.

Tad was playing in the hay when he heard a crash. He _____

_____

_____

_____

_____

_____

_____

Math Beacon

Color the circle on each corner.
Put an *X* on each side.
Fill in the boxes.

A triangle has ☐ sides and ☐ corners.

A square has ☐ sides and ☐ corners.

A rectangle has ☐ sides and ☐ corners.

LANGUAGE LODGE

Circle the letters that should be uppercase.

a cowboy named sam lives on a ranch. he works
hard to take care of the horses and cattle. each
day sam feeds the animals. he gives the animals
water too.

Rewrite the sentence adding uppercase letters and punctuation.

i love to read my book

_____

– – – – – – – – – – – – –

_____

Draw a picture of the sentence.

The rainbow shone over the field.

MATH JUNCTION

Write an equation for each word problem.
Solve it.

Tom had 7 baseball cards.
Bobby had 6 baseball cards.
How many baseball cards do
they have together?

☐ ☐ ☐ ☐ ☐   baseball cards

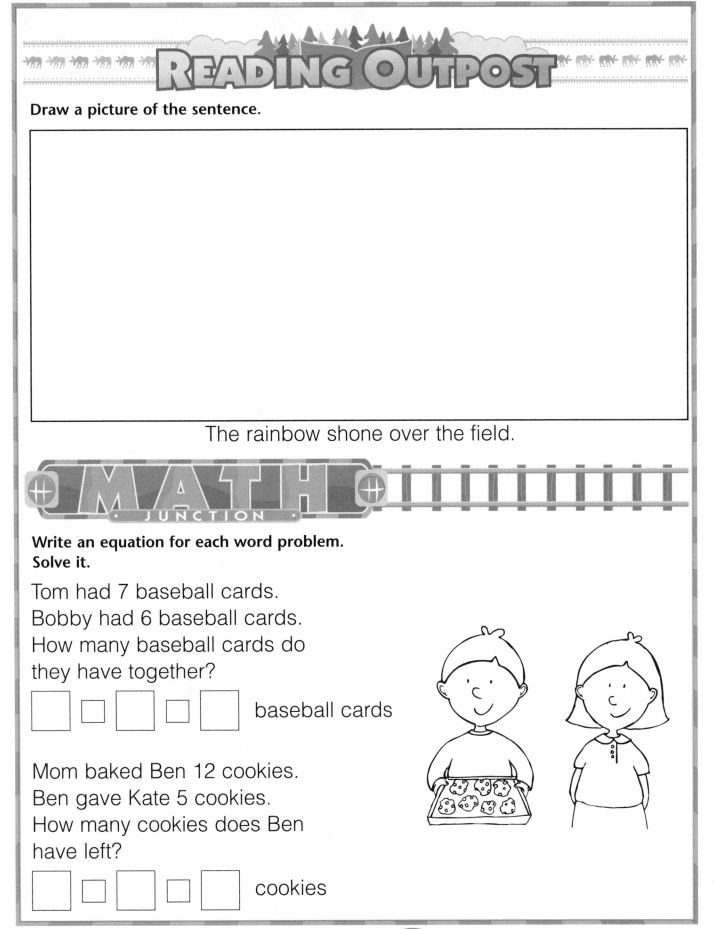

Mom baked Ben 12 cookies.
Ben gave Kate 5 cookies.
How many cookies does Ben
have left?

☐ ☐ ☐ ☐ ☐   cookies

Complete the other half of the picture.
Decorate and color.

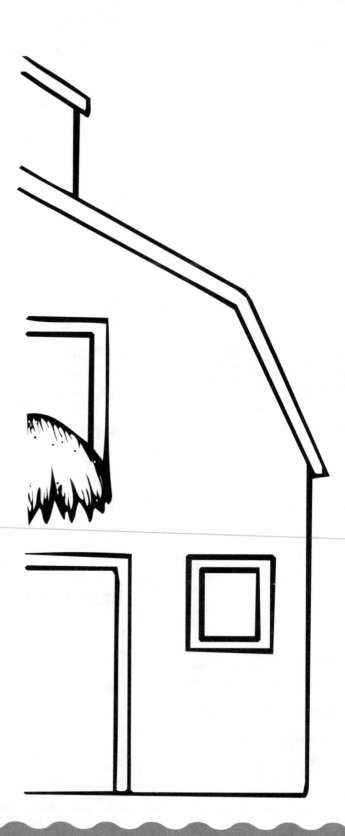

CONGRATULATIONS

to

for successfully completing

VACATION · STATIONS

1st Grade Going into 2nd

Parent's Signature

Date

ANSWER PAGES

Fact Harbor

Solve each fact. Write the facts that equal 12 inside the rope.

3 + 7 = **10**

6 + 7 = **13**

8 + 4 = **12**

7 + 5 = **12**

4 + 9 = **13**

6 + 5 = **11**

6 + 3 = **9**

8 + 7 = **15**

3 + 9 = **12**

4 + 7 = **11**

2 + 9 = **11**

4 + 8 = **12**

Inside rope:
7 + 5 = 12
3 + 9 = 12
4 + 8 = 12
8 + 4 = 12

12

Word Wayside

Color the words.

or as in 🌽 = blue

ar as in ⭐ = green

ir as in 🐦 = orange

stork	part	stir	horse
scarf	girl	port	far
short	firm	farm	shirt
barn	twirl	cord	torn

MATH JUNCTION

Write the number of tens and ones.

56 = **5** tens **6** ones

40 = **4** tens **0** ones

39 = **3** tens **9** ones

67 = **6** tens **7** ones

99 = **9** tens **9** ones

READING OUTPOST

Read the word families. Cross out the word that does *not* belong.

game	snake	made	gate
shame	rake	~~skate~~	late
~~lane~~	bake	shade	~~lake~~
flame	~~gate~~	grade	plate

Stagecoach Stations

How would you have traveled in the Old West? You might have ridden in a stagecoach. On a long trip you might have stopped at a home station.

At a home station travelers could get meals. At some stations the meals were good. At other stations the meals were not good. Travelers could also get a place to sleep. Often the beds were hard. Sometimes the rooms were unclean. But tired travelers were thankful for a place to sleep.

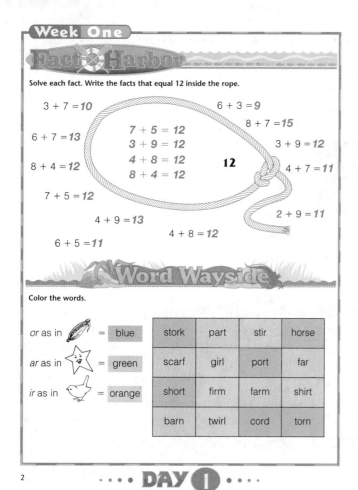

Circle the correct answer.

1. How might you have traveled in the Old West?
   (by bus, (by stagecoach))

2. Where did stagecoaches stop?
   ((home stations) coach stations)

3. Were the meals always good at a station?
   ((no,) yes)

4. What word means not clean?
   (hard, (unclean))

5. Why do you think the travelers were thankful for any bed and room?
   ((They were very tired.) They didn't like clean rooms.)

Math Beacon

Write the time.

4:30 **11:00** **12:30** **7:00**

5:00 **2:30** **9:00** **8:30**

Word Wayside

Clap the syllables and color the correct number of ☺s.

boxes	☺ ☺	wishbone	☺ ☺
rattle	☺ ☺	fish	☺ ☺
bone	☺ ☺	saddle	☺ ☺
cracker	☺ ☺	buckle	☺ ☺
rope	☺ ☺	branding	☺ ☺
cowboy	☺ ☺	west	☺ ☺

Math Beacon

Count the equal parts.
Write the number of equal parts.

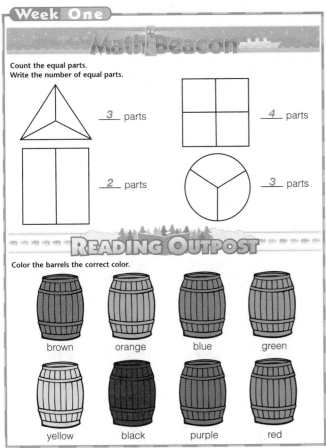

_3_ parts

_4_ parts

_2_ parts

_3_ parts

READING OUTPOST

Color the barrels the correct color.

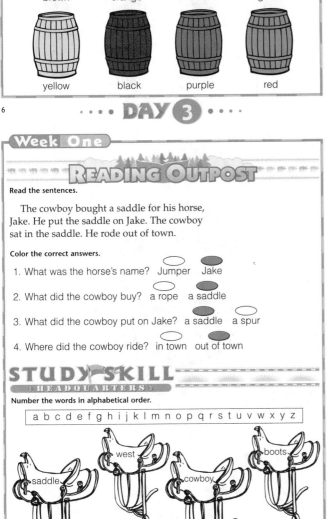

brown   orange   blue   green

yellow   black   purple   red

6   **· · · · DAY ③ · · · ·**

Fact Harbor

Solve the facts.

4	8	14	5	11
− 3	− 0	− 9	− 1	− 7
1	**8**	**5**	**4**	**4**

4	8	6	15	12
− 4	− 5	− 2	− 8	− 9
0	**3**	**4**	**7**	**3**

Word Wayside

Color the correct word for each sentence.

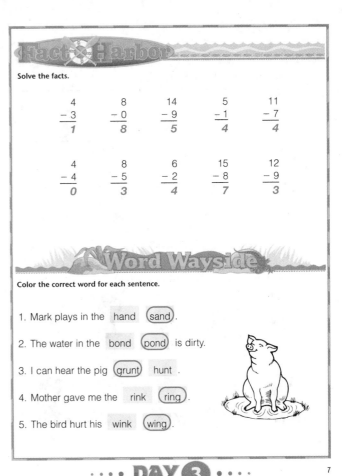

1. Mark plays in the   hand   (sand).

2. The water in the   bond   (pond)   is dirty.

3. I can hear the pig   (grunt)   hunt.

4. Mother gave me the   rink   (ring).

5. The bird hurt his   wink   (wing).

· · · · DAY ③ · · · ·   7

READING OUTPOST

Read the sentences.

The cowboy bought a saddle for his horse, Jake. He put the saddle on Jake. The cowboy sat in the saddle. He rode out of town.

Color the correct answers.

1. What was the horse's name?   Jumper   **Jake**

2. What did the cowboy buy?   a rope   **a saddle**

3. What did the cowboy put on Jake?   **a saddle**   a spur

4. Where did the cowboy ride?   in town   **out of town**

STUDY SKILL
HEADQUARTERS

Number the words in alphabetical order.

a b c d e f g h i j k l m n o p q r s t u v w x y z

west   boots

saddle   cowboy

_3_   _4_   _2_   _1_

8   **· · · · DAY ④ · · · ·**

Math Beacon

Circle the correct answer.

Quart = cup cup cup cup	(yes) no
Pint Pint = Quart	(yes) no
Pint = cup cup cup	yes (no)

Writer's Nook

Finish writing the story.

If I were going on a trip out West, I would _____

_____ _Answers will vary._ _____

_____

_____

_____

_____

· · · · DAY ④ · · · ·   9

Math Beacon

Color the shape that is the same size and shape as the first one.

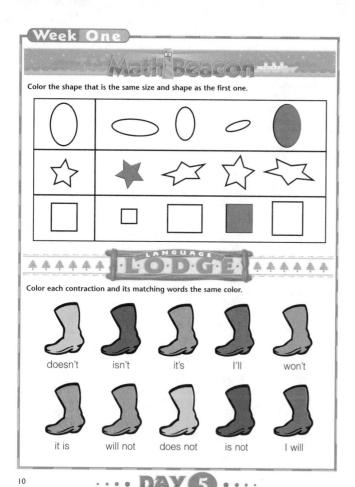

LANGUAGE LODGE

Color each contraction and its matching words the same color.

doesn't   isn't   it's   I'll   won't

it is   will not   does not   is not   I will

10

READING OUTPOST

Draw a picture of the sentence.

The cowboy fed his horse.

Fact Harbor

Complete each family of facts.

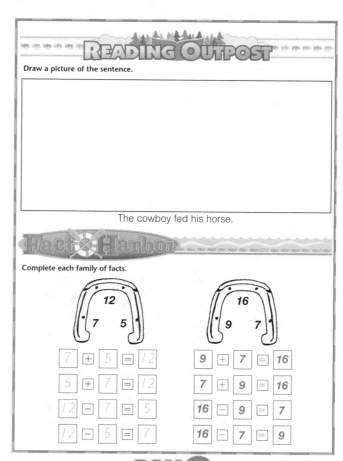

7	+	5	=	12
5	+	7	=	12
12	−	7	=	5
12	−	5	=	7

9	+	7	=	16
7	+	9	=	16
16	−	9	=	7
16	−	7	=	9

STATION BREAK

Find the words in the puzzle.

horse   saddle   cowboy   boot   brand   lasso   spurs   ranch

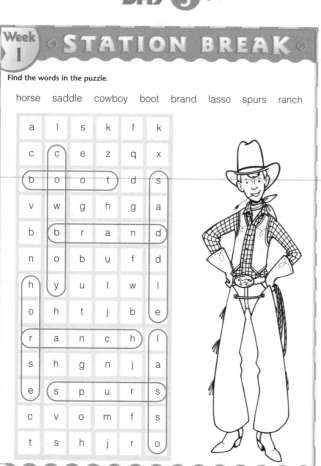

Fact Harbor

Color the names for 11 green.
Color the names for 10 orange.

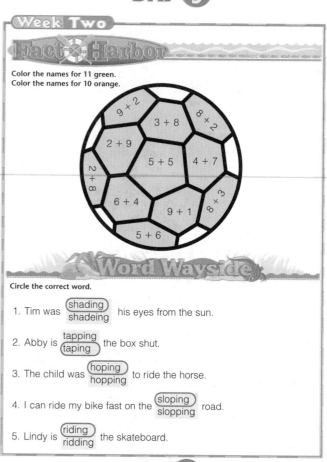

Word Wayside

Circle the correct word.

1. Tim was (shading / shadeing) his eyes from the sun.

2. Abby is (tapping / taping) the box shut.

3. The child was (hoping / hopping) to ride the horse.

4. I can ride my bike fast on the (sloping / slopping) road.

5. Lindy is (riding / ridding) the skateboard.

14

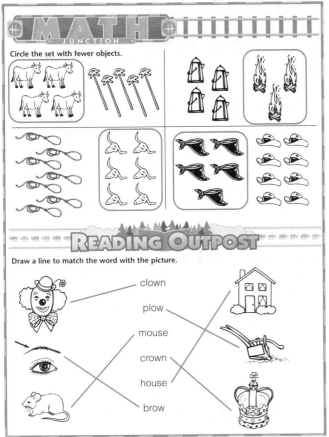

MATH JUNCTION

Circle the set with fewer objects.

READING OUTPOST

Draw a line to match the word with the picture.

clown

plow

mouse

crown

house

brow

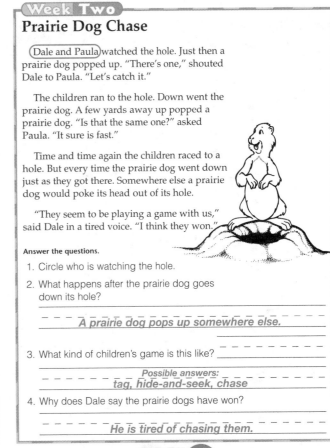

Prairie Dog Chase

Dale and Paula watched the hole. Just then a prairie dog popped up. "There's one," shouted Dale to Paula. "Let's catch it."

The children ran to the hole. Down went the prairie dog. A few yards away up popped a prairie dog. "Is that the same one?" asked Paula. "It sure is fast."

Time and time again the children raced to a hole. But every time the prairie dog went down just as they got there. Somewhere else a prairie dog would poke its head out of its hole.

"They seem to be playing a game with us," said Dale in a tired voice. "I think they won."

Answer the questions.

1. Circle who is watching the hole.

2. What happens after the prairie dog goes down its hole?
   A prairie dog pops up somewhere else.

3. What kind of children's game is this like?
   Possible answers:
   tag, hide-and-seek, chase

4. Why does Dale say the prairie dogs have won?
   He is tired of chasing them.

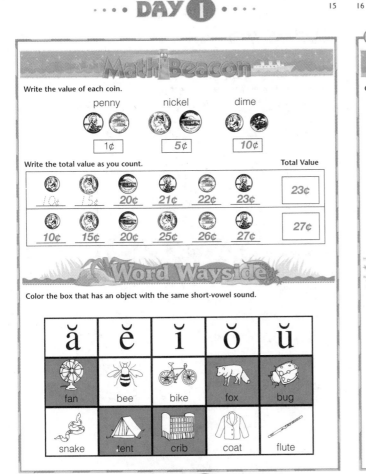

Math Beacon

Write the value of each coin.

penny	nickel	dime
1¢	5¢	10¢

Write the total value as you count. Total Value

10¢	15¢	20¢	21¢	22¢	23¢	23¢
10¢	15¢	20¢	25¢	26¢	27¢	27¢

Word Wayside

Color the box that has an object with the same short-vowel sound.

ă	ě	ǐ	ǒ	ǔ
fan	bee	bike	fox	bug
snake	tent	crib	coat	flute

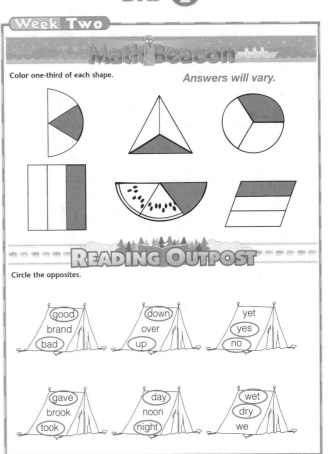

Math Beacon

Color one-third of each shape.   *Answers will vary.*

READING OUTPOST

Circle the opposites.

good
brand
bad

down
over
up

yet
yes
no

gave
brook
took

day
noon
night

wet
dry
we

Fact Harbor

Color the correct oval.

12−6 =	7	5	6		
10−4 =	6	8	7		
11−6 =	6	7	5		
9−2 =	7	6	8		
8−5 =	2	3	1		
10−7 =	3	2	4		

13−4 =	8	9	7
12−4 =	7	8	9
10−6 =	4	3	5
12−3 =	8	10	9
11−4 =	6	8	7
11−8 =	2	3	4

Word Wayside

Circle the beginning or ending *st*.

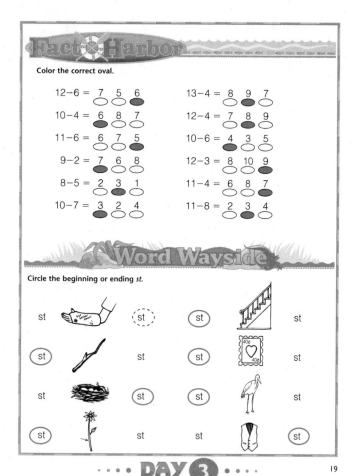

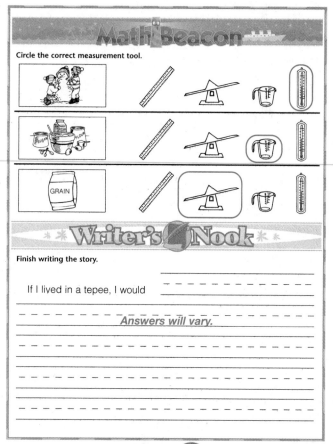

READING OUTPOST

Read the sentences. Mark the correct answers.

1. The horse wanted hay.
   ○ He was not hungry.
   ● He was hungry.
2. Father cuts the logs for the fireplace.
   ● The logs are too big.
   ○ The logs are too small.
3. Anna planted the seeds.
   ○ She wanted fish.
   ● She wanted flowers.
4. Ellen read the books many times.
   ● She likes to read.
   ○ She does not like to read.

STUDY SKILL
HEADQUARTERS

Follow the directions.
1. Write your first name.
2. Draw a picture of yourself.
3. Put a cowboy hat and boots on your picture.

_____
_____

Me

Math Beacon

Circle the correct measurement tool.

Writer's Nook

Finish writing the story.

If I lived in a tepee, I would _____

Answers will vary.

MATH JUNCTION

Solve each problem using the place-value frame.

Tens	Ones
3	2
+ 2	4
5	6

Tens	Ones
7	4
+ 2	3
9	7

Tens	Ones
6	3
+ 3	5
9	8

Tens	Ones
4	3
+ 4	3
8	6

Tens	Ones
2	8
+ 4	1
6	9

Tens	Ones
1	2
+ 8	6
9	8

LANGUAGE LODGE

Circle the letters that should be uppercase. (There are two in each sentence.)

1. tuesday is tony's birthday.
2. bill finley is our bus driver.
3. dad gave me a new bible.
4. i will visit you on thursday.
5. ann's birthday is in september.
6. jason likes to play with samuel.
7. our school starts in august.

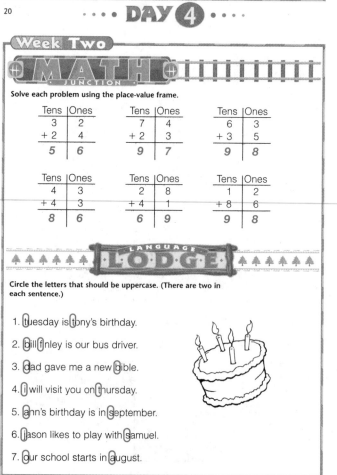

Draw a picture of the sentence.

The cowboy cooked his food over a fire.

Fact Harbor

Complete each family of facts.

5	+	6	=	11
6	+	5	=	11
11	−	5	=	6
11	−	6	=	5

5	+	3	=	8
3	+	5	=	8
8	−	5	=	3
8	−	3	=	5

· · · · **DAY 5** · · · ·

23

24

Circle the odd numbers. Draw a line to connect the odd numbers and help the prairie dog get to his hole.

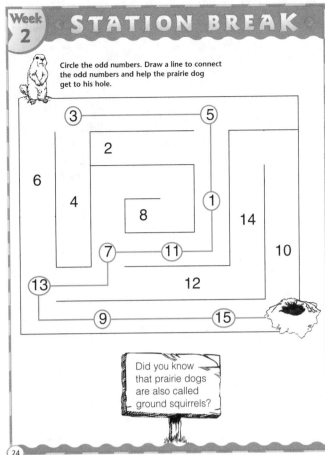

Did you know that prairie dogs are also called ground squirrels?

Week Three

Fact Harbor

Complete the charts.

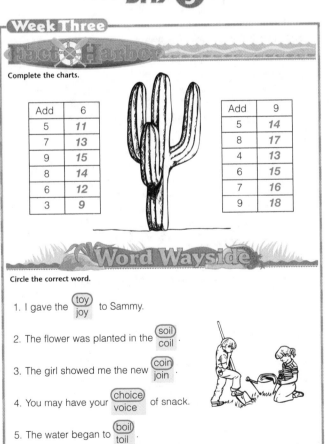

Add	6
5	11
7	13
9	15
8	14
6	12
3	9

Add	9
5	14
8	17
4	13
6	15
7	16
9	18

Word Wayside

Circle the correct word.

1. I gave the (toy) / joy to Sammy.

2. The flower was planted in the (soil) / coil.

3. The girl showed me the new (coin) / join.

4. You may have your (choice) / voice of snack.

5. The water began to (boil) / toil.

26

· · · · **DAY 1** · · · ·

Write the missing numbers.

25	26	27	43	44	45
39	40	41	58	59	60
68	69	70	49	50	51
97	98	99	32	33	34

READING OUTPOST

Color the sets of rhyming words.

tool — purple
book — yellow
noon — red
zoom — blue

· · · · **DAY 1** · · · ·

27

Texas Longhorns

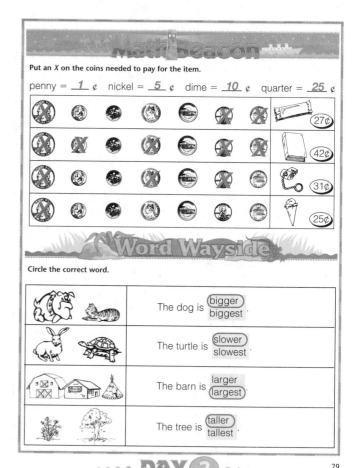

How do you think Texas Longhorn cattle got their name? Their long horns make them easy to spot. Some Longhorns have straight horns. Others have horns that twist or curl. Some Longhorns have horns eight feet long!

Most Longhorns are found in the West. Cattle with long horns need good food. Longhorns eat well on grasses growing on the plains of the West.

Answer the questions.

1. How did the Texas Longhorn get its name?

   It has long horns.

2. How long can their horns get? _eight feet_

3. Why is the West a good place for Longhorns to live?

   There is good grass for them to eat.

4. Why would a Texas Longhorn not make a good pet?

   Answers will vary.

28

• • • • DAY 2 • • • •

Math Beacon

Put an *X* on the coins needed to pay for the item.

penny = _1_ ¢   nickel = _5_ ¢   dime = _10_ ¢   quarter = _25_ ¢

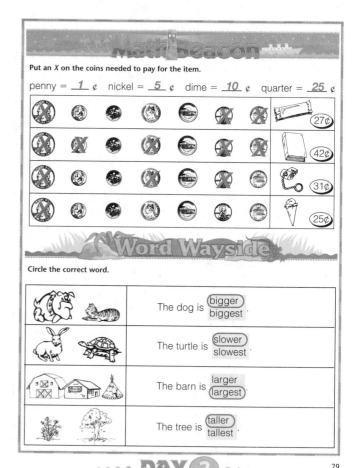

Word Wayside

Circle the correct word.

	The dog is (bigger) biggest .
	The turtle is (slower) slowest .
	The barn is larger (largest) .
	The tree is (taller) tallest .

• • • • DAY 2 • • • •   29

Math Beacon

Circle one-half of the set.

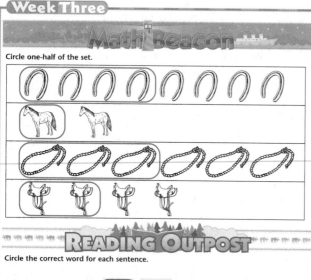

Reading Outpost

Circle the correct word for each sentence.

1. Each day I do my (chores) chairs .

2. How far can Tim know (throw) the ball?

3. The children enjoy hearing a good store (story) .

4. I took my dog to Grandmother's (house) horse .

5. Adam (tore) store   his new pants on the fence.

6. Jess will know (show) Dan his pet turtle.

30

• • • • DAY 3 • • • •

MATH JUNCTION

Write a number sentence for each word problem.

1. Joyce has 10 marbles.
   Dana has 4 marbles.
   How many more marbles does Joyce have?

   _10_ − _4_ = _6_ marbles

2. Mike had 12 toy cars.
   He gives 5 cars to Sam.
   How many toy cars does Mike have left?

   _12_ − _5_ = _7_ toy cars

Word Wayside

For each *c*, write *s* if it has a sound like *ice* and *k* if it has a sound like *Kate*.

camp	_k_		cute	_k_
cake	_k_		cowboy	_k_
fence	_s_		cent	_s_
cat	_k_		cot	_k_
lacy	_s_		code	_k_
nice	_s_		candy	_k_

• • • • DAY 3 • • • •   31

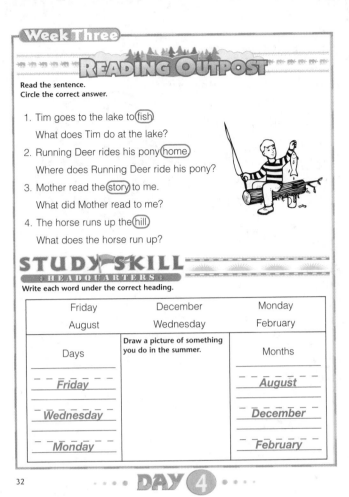

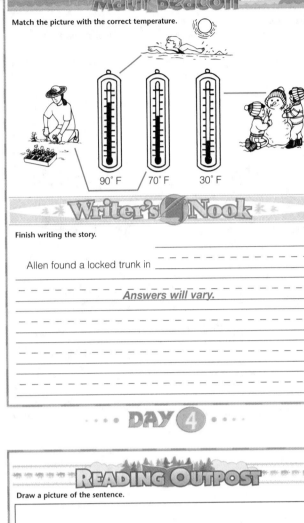

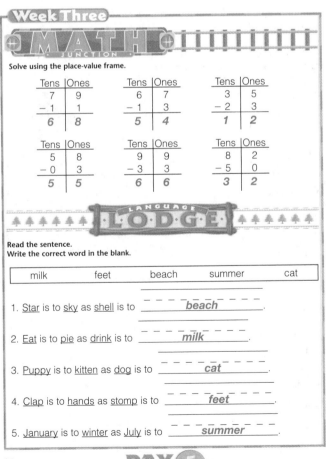

READING OUTPOST

Read the sentence.
Circle the correct answer.

1. Tim goes to the lake to (fish)

   What does Tim do at the lake?

2. Running Deer rides his pony (home)

   Where does Running Deer ride his pony?

3. Mother read the (story) to me.

   What did Mother read to me?

4. The horse runs up the (hill)

   What does the horse run up?

STUDY SKILL
☀ HEADQUARTERS ☀

Write each word under the correct heading.

Friday	December	Monday
August	Wednesday	February

Days	Draw a picture of something you do in the summer.	Months
Friday		*August*
Wednesday		*December*
Monday		*February*

Math Beacon

Match the picture with the correct temperature.

90° F   70° F   30° F

Writer's Nook

Finish writing the story.

Allen found a locked trunk in _____

_____

Answers will vary.

_____

_____

_____

_____

MATH JUNCTION

Solve using the place-value frame.

Tens	Ones
7	9
− 1	1
6	*8*

Tens	Ones
6	7
− 1	3
5	*4*

Tens	Ones
3	5
− 2	3
1	*2*

Tens	Ones
5	8
− 0	3
5	*5*

Tens	Ones
9	9
− 3	3
6	*6*

Tens	Ones
8	2
− 5	0
3	*2*

LANGUAGE LODGE

Read the sentence.
Write the correct word in the blank.

milk	feet	beach	summer	cat

1. Star is to sky as shell is to ___*beach*___ .

2. Eat is to pie as drink is to ___*milk*___ .

3. Puppy is to kitten as dog is to ___*cat*___ .

4. Clap is to hands as stomp is to ___*feet*___ .

5. January is to winter as July is to ___*summer*___ .

READING OUTPOST

Draw a picture of the sentence.

The puppy has a bone.

Fact Harbor

Complete each family of facts.

$9 + 8 = 17$
$8 + 9 = 17$
$17 − 8 = 9$
$17 − 9 = 8$

$8 + 7 = 15$
$7 + 8 = 15$
$15 − 8 = 7$
$15 − 7 = 8$

STATION BREAK

Find the hidden objects.

horseshoe   horse's head   Indian headdress
cowboy hat   saddle
spur   branding iron

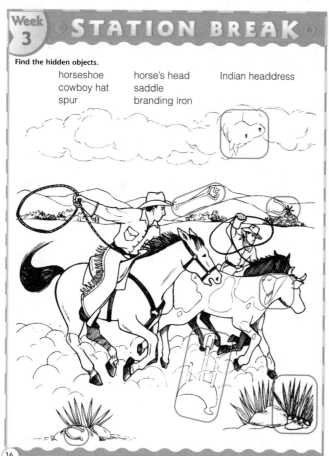

36

Fact Harbor

Color the facts that equal the number in the center.

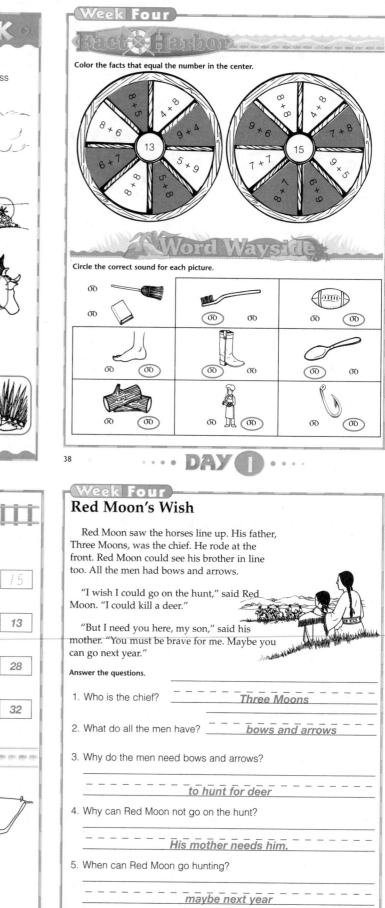

Word Wayside

Circle the correct sound for each picture.

38 · · · · DAY 1 · · · ·

MATH JUNCTION

Write the number of tens and ones.
Write the number.

1 ten	5 ones	15
1 ten	3 ones	13
2 ten	8 ones	28
3 ten	2 ones	32

READING OUTPOST

Draw a line from the picture to the correct word.

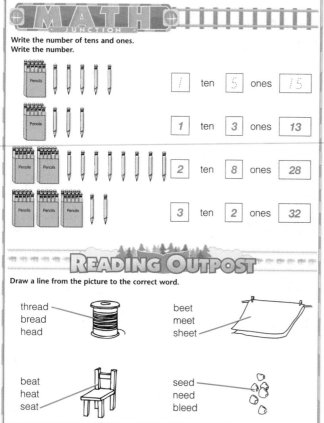

thread   beet
bread   meet
head   sheet

beat   seed
heat   need
seat   bleed

· · · · DAY 1 · · · ·

39

Red Moon's Wish

Red Moon saw the horses line up. His father, Three Moons, was the chief. He rode at the front. Red Moon could see his brother in line too. All the men had bows and arrows.

"I wish I could go on the hunt," said Red Moon. "I could kill a deer."

"But I need you here, my son," said his mother. "You must be brave for me. Maybe you can go next year."

Answer the questions.

1. Who is the chief? _*Three Moons*_

2. What do all the men have? _*bows and arrows*_

3. Why do the men need bows and arrows?
*to hunt for deer*

4. Why can Red Moon not go on the hunt?
*His mother needs him.*

5. When can Red Moon go hunting?
*maybe next year*

40   · · · · DAY 2 · · · ·

Math Beacon

Write the days of the week in order.

Saturday	Wednesday	Monday	Thursday
Tuesday	Friday	Sunday	

1. *Sunday*
2. *Monday*
3. *Tuesday*
4. *Wednesday*
5. *Thursday*
6. *Friday*
7. *Saturday*

Word Wayside

Draw lines to form compound words.

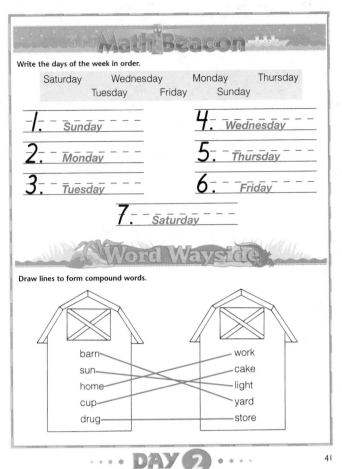

barn — work
sun — cake
home — light
cup — yard
drug — store

Math Beacon

What comes next? Complete the pattern.

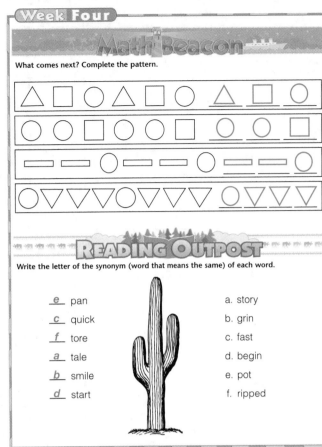

Reading Outpost

Write the letter of the synonym (word that means the same) of each word.

_e_ pan
_c_ quick
_f_ tore
_a_ tale
_b_ smile
_d_ start

a. story
b. grin
c. fast
d. begin
e. pot
f. ripped

···· DAY 2 ···· 41

42 ···· DAY 3 ····

Fact Harbor

Solve the facts.

$10 - 2 = \boxed{8}$ $6 - 6 = \boxed{0}$ $7 - 1 = \boxed{6}$

$11 - 7 = \boxed{4}$ $15 - 8 = \boxed{7}$ $13 - 9 = \boxed{4}$

$12 - 3 = \boxed{9}$ $14 - 5 = \boxed{9}$ $5 - 3 = \boxed{2}$

$4 - 3 = \boxed{1}$ $16 - 8 = \boxed{8}$ $11 - 4 = \boxed{7}$

Word Wayside

Circle the silent letter(s) in each word.

sight   wrist   sign
knob   crumb
lamb   light
wrench   wrap

Reading Outpost

Read the sentences. Circle the correct answers.

1. Mary won the race.
   Mary is (fast) slow .
2. Susan helped Tom ride a bike.
   Susan was (kind) unkind .
3. Andy shared his Bible with his friend.
   Andy is selfish (unselfish) .
4. Alan jumped up and down with joy.
   Alan was (happy) sad .

STUDY SKILL
HEADQUARTERS

Use the map to fill in the blanks.

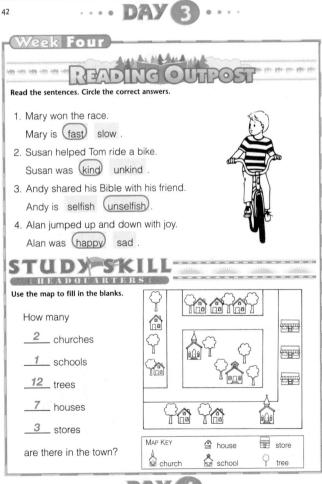

How many

_2_ churches
_1_ schools
_12_ trees
_7_ houses
_3_ stores

are there in the town?

MAP KEY
🏠 house   🗄 store
⛪ church   🏫 school   🌳 tree

···· DAY 3 ···· 43

44 ···· DAY 4 ····

Math Beacon

Start at the ●. Count the objects around each picture. Write your answer in the box.

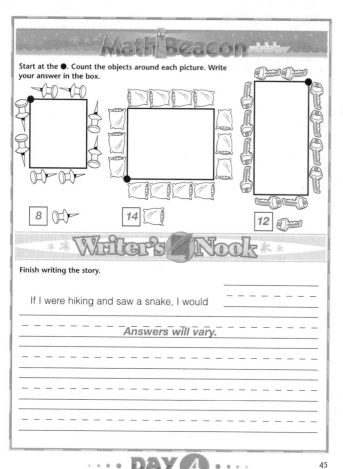

| 8 | 14 | 12 |

Writer's Nook

Finish writing the story.

If I were hiking and saw a snake, I would _____

_____ Answers will vary. _____

Math Beacon

Color.

circle – yellow
square – blue
rectangle – green
triangle – orange

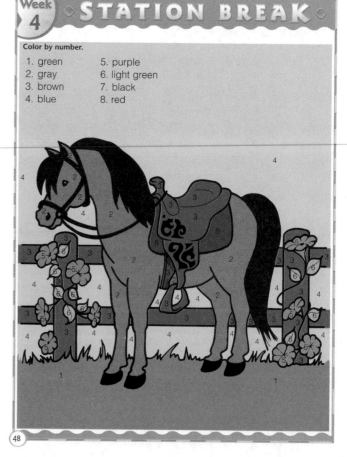

LANGUAGE LODGE

Add the correct punctuation (. or ?) to each sentence.

1. My Bible is on the table .
2. Who made the cookies for the party ?
3. The horse ran fast up the hill .
4. How high can you jump ?
5. Who made you ?
6. God made me and all things .
7. Where is the ball for the game ?
8. We need another girl for our team .

· · · · DAY 4 · · · ·

· · · · DAY 5 · · · ·

READING OUTPOST

Draw a picture of the sentence.

A big frog is on the log.

Fact Harbor

Write an equation for each word problem. Solve it.

Seth baked 7 muffins.
Anna baked 6 muffins.
How many did they bake together?

| 7 | + | 6 | = | 13 | muffins

Ben ate 3 eggs.
Beth ate 2 eggs.
How many eggs did they both eat?

| 3 | + | 2 | = | 5 | eggs

Week 4 · STATION BREAK ·

Color by number.

1. green   5. purple
2. gray   6. light green
3. brown   7. black
4. blue   8. red

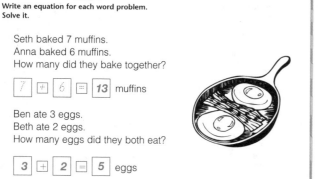

· · · · DAY 5 · · · ·

Math Beacon

Write the value of each coin.

= __1¢__   = __5¢__   = __10¢__   = __25¢__

Put an *X* on the coins that equal a quarter.

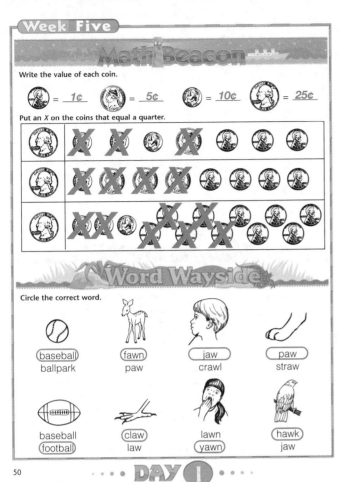

Word Wayside

Circle the correct word.

(baseball)   (fawn)   (jaw)   (paw)
ballpark   paw   crawl   straw

baseball   (claw)   lawn   (hawk)
(football)   law   (yawn)   jaw

50

MATH JUNCTION

Count by 2s.
Write the missing numbers.

2	4	6	8	10
12	14	16	18	20
22	24	26	28	30
32	34	36	38	40
42	44	46	48	50

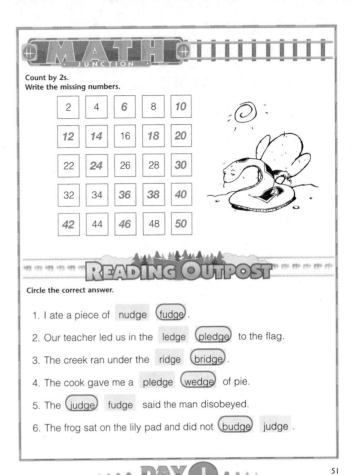

READING OUTPOST

Circle the correct answer.

1. I ate a piece of   nudge   (fudge) .

2. Our teacher led us in the   ledge   (pledge)   to the flag.

3. The creek ran under the   ridge   (bridge) .

4. The cook gave me a   pledge   (wedge)   of pie.

5. The   (judge)   fudge   said the man disobeyed.

6. The frog sat on the lily pad and did not   (budge)   judge .

51

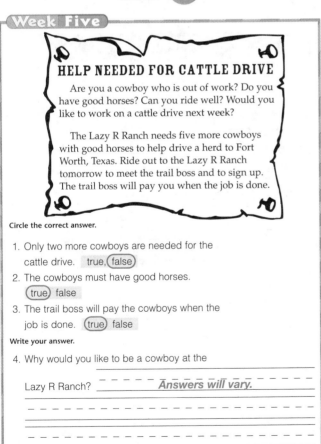

HELP NEEDED FOR CATTLE DRIVE

Are you a cowboy who is out of work? Do you have good horses? Can you ride well? Would you like to work on a cattle drive next week?

The Lazy R Ranch needs five more cowboys with good horses to help drive a herd to Fort Worth, Texas. Ride out to the Lazy R Ranch tomorrow to meet the trail boss and to sign up. The trail boss will pay you when the job is done.

Circle the correct answer.

1. Only two more cowboys are needed for the cattle drive.   true, (false)

2. The cowboys must have good horses.
   (true)   false

3. The trail boss will pay the cowboys when the job is done.   (true)   false

Write your answer.

4. Why would you like to be a cowboy at the

Lazy R Ranch? _____ *Answers will vary.* _____

52

MATH JUNCTION

Write an equation for each word problem. Solve it.

1. There are 7 balls in the box.
   Trent adds 2 more balls.
   How many balls are there in all?

   __7__ + __2__ = __9__ balls

2. Sandy has 5 yellow flowers.
   She cut 4 more flowers.
   How many flowers does Sandy have in all?

   __5__ + __4__ = __9__ flowers

Word Wayside

Add *s* or *es* to the words. Remember to add *es* after *ch, sh, s,* and *z.*

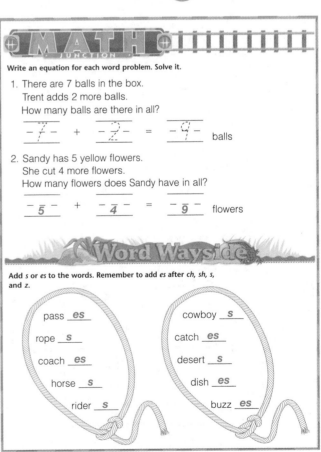

pass __es__   cowboy __s__
rope __s__   catch __es__
coach __es__   desert __s__
horse __s__   dish __es__
rider __s__   buzz __es__

53

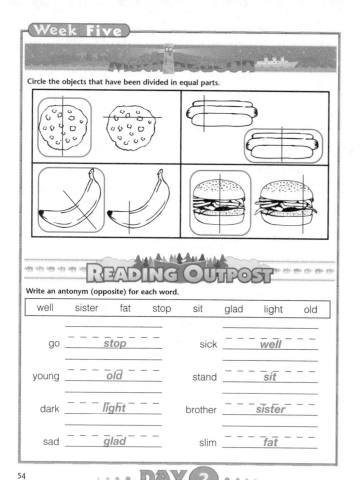

Math Beacon

Circle the objects that have been divided in equal parts.

READING OUTPOST

Write an antonym (opposite) for each word.

well	sister	fat	stop	sit	glad	light	old

go ___ stop ___   sick ___ well ___

young ___ old ___   stand ___ sit ___

dark ___ light ___   brother ___ sister ___

sad ___ glad ___   slim ___ fat ___

Fact Harbor

Solve the facts.

$$\begin{array}{r} 3 \\ -2 \\ \hline 1 \end{array} \qquad \begin{array}{r} 7 \\ -5 \\ \hline 2 \end{array} \qquad \begin{array}{r} 7 \\ -6 \\ \hline 1 \end{array} \qquad \begin{array}{r} 8 \\ -2 \\ \hline 6 \end{array} \qquad \begin{array}{r} 5 \\ -5 \\ \hline 0 \end{array}$$

$$\begin{array}{r} 5 \\ -4 \\ \hline 1 \end{array} \qquad \begin{array}{r} 6 \\ -5 \\ \hline 1 \end{array} \qquad \begin{array}{r} 9 \\ -7 \\ \hline 2 \end{array} \qquad \begin{array}{r} 4 \\ -3 \\ \hline 1 \end{array} \qquad \begin{array}{r} 10 \\ -4 \\ \hline 6 \end{array}$$

Word Wayside

Circle the correct beginning or ending sound.

c   (ck)   (c)   ck   c   (ck)

c   (ck)   (c)   ck   (c)   ck

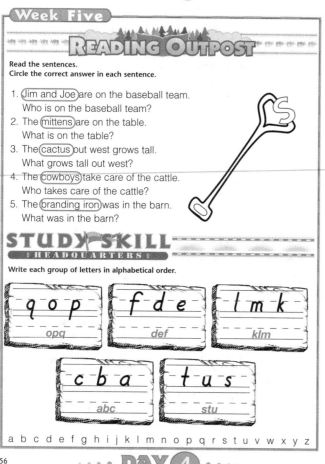

READING OUTPOST

Read the sentences.
Circle the correct answer in each sentence.

1. Jim and Joe are on the baseball team.
   Who is on the baseball team?
2. The mittens are on the table.
   What is on the table?
3. The cactus out west grows tall.
   What grows tall out west?
4. The cowboys take care of the cattle.
   Who takes care of the cattle?
5. The branding iron was in the barn.
   What was in the barn?

STUDY SKILL
HEADQUARTERS

Write each group of letters in alphabetical order.

q o p → opq

f d e → def

l m k → klm

c b a → abc

t u s → stu

a b c d e f g h i j k l m n o p q r s t u v w x y z

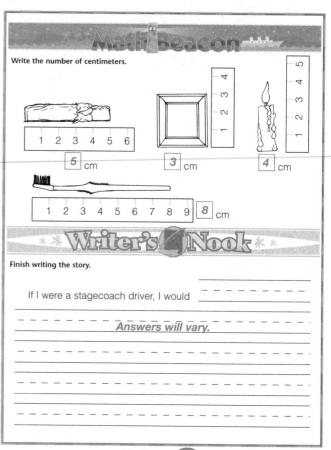

Math Beacon

Write the number of centimeters.

1 2 3 4 5 6   5 cm

3 cm

4 cm

1 2 3 4 5 6 7 8 9   8 cm

Writer's Nook

Finish writing the story.

If I were a stagecoach driver, I would ___

___ Answers will vary. ___

MATH JUNCTION

Solve each problem using the place-value frame.

Tens	Ones
1	5
+ 2	3
3	**8**

Tens	Ones
2	1
+ 3	8
5	**9**

Tens	Ones
3	5
+ 6	0
9	**5**

Tens	Ones
4	6
+ 3	3
7	**9**

Tens	Ones
7	0
+ 2	0
9	**0**

Tens	Ones
8	8
+ 1	1
9	**9**

Tens	Ones
6	2
+ 0	7
6	**9**

Tens	Ones
3	2
+ 5	6
8	**8**

LANGUAGE LODGE

Use words from the boxes to complete these compound words.

lace hive day drop ball

rain _drop_

shoe _lace_

birth _day_

meat _ball_

bee _hive_

flake trap shore box town

mail _box_

sea _shore_

mouse _trap_

down _town_

snow _flake_

DAY 5

READING OUTPOST

Draw a picture of the sentence.

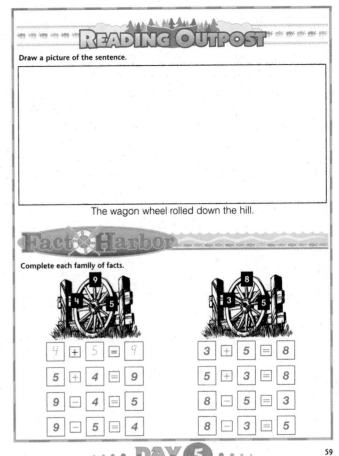

The wagon wheel rolled down the hill.

Fact Harbor

Complete each family of facts.

9 / 4 / 5

4 + 5 = 9

5 + 4 = 9

9 − 4 = 5

9 − 5 = 4

8 / 3 / 5

3 + 5 = 8

5 + 3 = 8

8 − 5 = 3

8 − 3 = 5

DAY 5

STATION BREAK

Decorate and color each thumbprint.

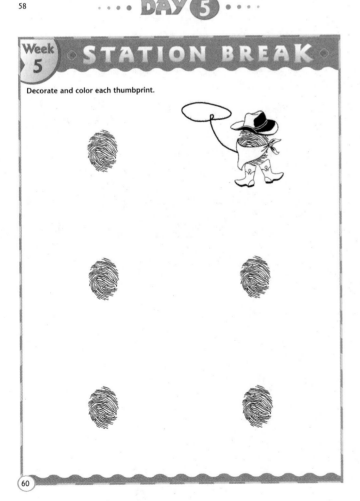

Fact Harbor

Color the correct oval.

9 + 9	7 + 7	5 + 5	9 + 8	7 + 5	4 + 7
17	**14**	**10**	**17**	13	**11**
18	13	11	16	**12**	12

8 + 8	6 + 6	4 + 4	8 + 6	5 + 8	3 + 8
16	11	7	15	**13**	10
15	**12**	**8**	**14**	14	**11**

Word Wayside

Circle the correct word.

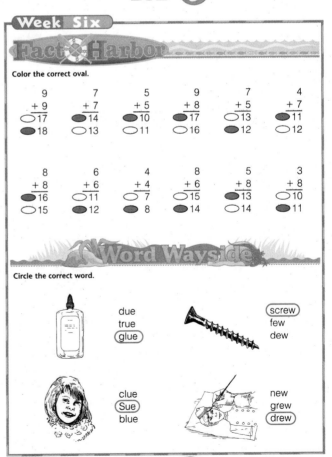

due
true
(glue)

screw
few
dew

clue
(Sue)
blue

new
grew
(drew)

DAY 1

MATH JUNCTION

Write the tens and ones.

35 = __3__ tens __5__ ones   99 = __9__ tens __9__ ones

51 = __5__ tens __1__ ones   79 = __7__ tens __9__ ones

55 = __5__ tens __5__ ones   86 = __8__ tens __6__ ones

37 = __3__ tens __7__ ones   48 = __4__ tens __8__ ones

18 = __1__ tens __8__ ones   14 = __1__ tens __4__ ones

60 = __6__ tens __0__ ones   28 = __2__ tens __8__ ones

READING OUTPOST

Add a word to each word family.

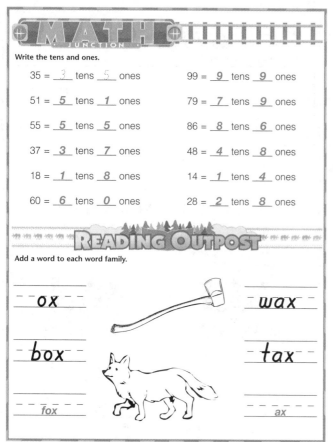

ox

box

fox

wax

tax

ax

· · · · **DAY 1** · · · ·

63

64

A Plant that Heals

The cactus is a desert plant. Most cactus plants are light green or yellow. They can be short and round like balls. Or they can be tall with thin arms. Some have pretty flowers. But don't try to pick one! Cactus plants also have prickly spines that can stick you.

Many kinds of cactus plants can be used for healing. Inside the prickly pear cactus is a sap. This sap can help to heal sunburn or snakebite. Some cactus plants can help treat pain. But first you have to take their spines off!

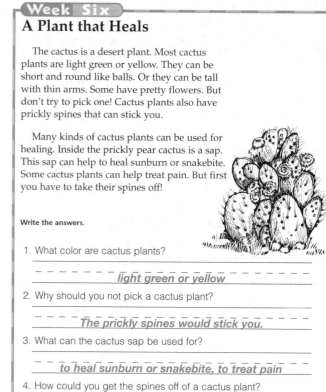

Write the answers.

1. What color are cactus plants?

light green or yellow

2. Why should you not pick a cactus plant?

The prickly spines would stick you.

3. What can the cactus sap be used for?

to heal sunburn or snakebite, to treat pain

4. How could you get the spines off of a cactus plant?

Accept any answer.

· · · · **DAY 2** · · · ·

Math Beacon

Write the hour.
Count by 5s and write the minutes.

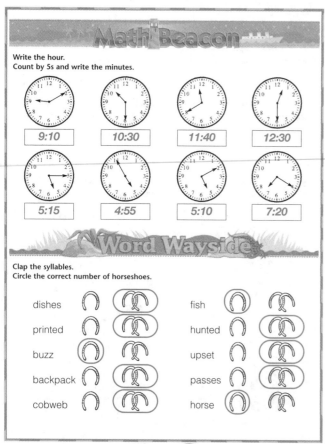

| 9:10 | 10:30 | 11:40 | 12:30 |

| 5:15 | 4:55 | 5:10 | 7:20 |

Word Wayside

Clap the syllables.
Circle the correct number of horseshoes.

dishes   fish

printed   hunted

buzz   upset

backpack   passes

cobweb   horse

· · · **DAY 2** · · · ·

65

Math Beacon

Color the blocks according to the key.

| halves | thirds | fourths |
| green | blue | red |

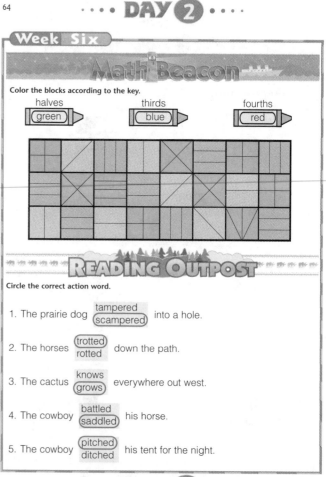

READING OUTPOST

Circle the correct action word.

1. The prairie dog ~~tampered~~ **(scampered)** into a hole.

2. The horses **(trotted)** ~~rotted~~ down the path.

3. The cactus ~~knows~~ **(grows)** everywhere out west.

4. The cowboy ~~battled~~ **(saddled)** his horse.

5. The cowboy **(pitched)** ~~ditched~~ his tent for the night.

66

· · · · **DAY 3** · · · ·

Fact Harbor

Solve the facts.

11 − 5 **6**	12 − 7 **5**	12 − 3 **9**	9 − 1 **8**
17 − 9 **8**	5 − 4 **1**	10 − 2 **8**	7 − 6 **1**
10 − 3 **7**	6 − 2 **4**	7 − 1 **6**	13 − 6 **7**

Word Wayside

Circle the beginning or ending *th*.

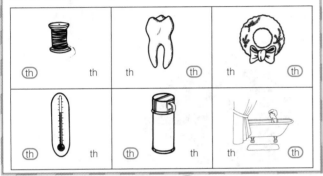

(th) th | th (th) | th (th)
(th) th | (th) th | th (th)

READING OUTPOST

Read the sentences.
Draw a line from each picture to the correct sentence.

The cowboy roped the bull.
The cowboy roped the horse.

The bug crawled on the ground.
The bug crawled on the leaf.

The toy dog is on wheels.
The toy dog is under the bed.

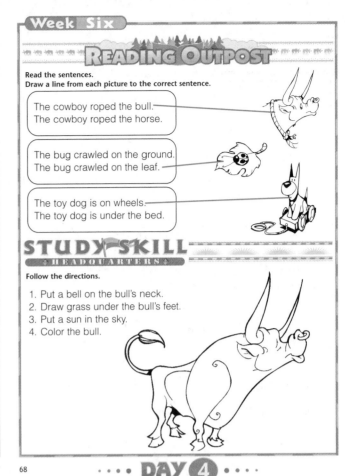

STUDY SKILL HEADQUARTERS

Follow the directions.

1. Put a bell on the bull's neck.
2. Draw grass under the bull's feet.
3. Put a sun in the sky.
4. Color the bull.

Math Beacon

Fill in the correct oval.

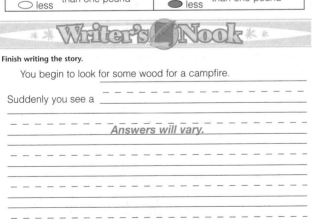

○ more than one pound
● less

● more than one pound
○ less

● more than one pound
○ less

○ more than one pound
● less

Writer's Nook

Finish writing the story.

You begin to look for some wood for a campfire.

Suddenly you see a _____

_____
Answers will vary.

Math Beacon

What comes next?

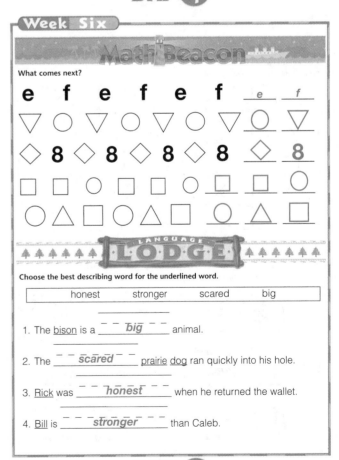

e f e f e f *e* *f*

LANGUAGE LODGE

Choose the best describing word for the underlined word.

honest	stronger	scared	big

1. The <u>bison</u> is a ___ *big* ___ animal.

2. The ___ *scared* ___ <u>prairie dog</u> ran quickly into his hole.

3. <u>Rick</u> was ___ *honest* ___ when he returned the wallet.

4. <u>Bill</u> is ___ *stronger* ___ than Caleb.

Draw a picture of the sentence.

The puppy is wearing a hat.

MATH JUNCTION

Write a number sentence for each word problem.

1. Ted dug up 12 worms.
   He lost 4 worms.
   How many worms does he have left?

   _12_ – _4_ = _8_ worms

2. Deb had 9 goldfish.
   She gave Sarah 4.
   How many goldfish does she have now?

   _9_ – _4_ = _5_ goldfish

···· DAY 5 ····   71

72

Look at the pictures.
Circle what is missing.
Draw the missing item in the picture.
You may color the pictures.

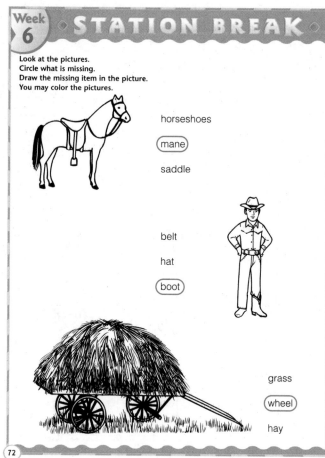

horseshoes
(mane)
saddle

belt
hat
(boot)

grass
(wheel)
hay

74

Week Seven

Fact Harbor

Follow the directions to solve the facts.

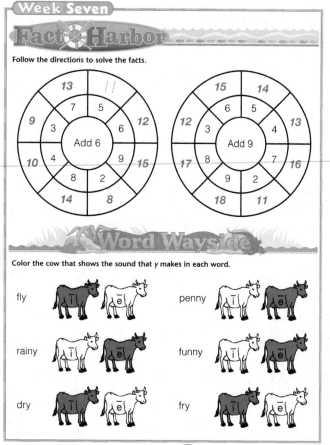

Add 6

13   7   5   ///
9   3   6   12
10   4   9   15
8   2
14   8

Add 9

15   14
12   6   5   13
17   3   4   16
8   7
9   2
18   11

Word Wayside

Color the cow that shows the sound that *y* makes in each word.

fly   penny

rainy   funny

dry   fry

···· DAY 1 ····

MATH JUNCTION

Count from 1 to 50.
Write the missing numbers.

1	2	3	4	5	6	7	8	9	10
11	12	13	14	15	16	17	18	19	20
21	22	23	24	25	26	27	28	29	30
31	32	33	34	35	36	37	38	39	40
41	42	43	44	45	46	47	48	49	50

READING OUTPOST

Read each word family. Draw a line from each picture to the correct word.

lube
tube
cube

flute
mute
cute

June
prune
tune

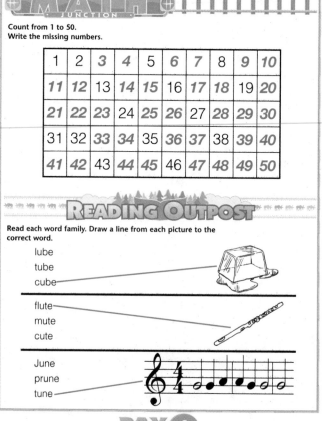

···· DAY 1 ····   75

Driving a Stagecoach

1. Do you think you would like to drive a stagecoach? Coach drivers had a hard job. They had to know all about horses. They drove in the ice and snow. Sometimes they had to drive in the dark.

2. Each driver would cover one part of the trail. He needed to know the roads well. Sometimes the roads went up the sides of the hills. Sometimes the roads went along cliffs. The driver had a risky job.

Read the story.
Write the number of the paragraph above that gives the information.

2	Sometimes the roads went along cliffs.
2	The driver had a risky job.
1	Coach drivers had a hard job.
2	Drivers needed to know the roads well.
1	Sometimes they had to drive in the dark.
1	They drove in ice and snow.

Tell why you would like to drive a stagecoach.

_____

Answers will vary.

_____

76   ···· DAY **2** ····

Put an X on the coins needed.

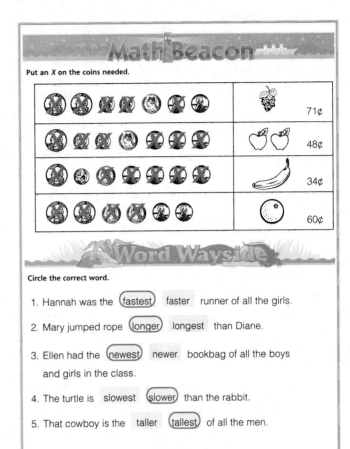

🍇 grapes	71¢
🍎🍎 apples	48¢
🍌 banana	34¢
🍊 orange	60¢

Word Wayside

Circle the correct word.

1. Hannah was the (fastest) faster runner of all the girls.

2. Mary jumped rope (longer) longest than Diane.

3. Ellen had the (newest) newer bookbag of all the boys and girls in the class.

4. The turtle is slowest (slower) than the rabbit.

5. That cowboy is the taller (tallest) of all the men.

···· DAY **2** ····   77

Color the hats according to the key.

outside	inside	on
green	brown	yellow

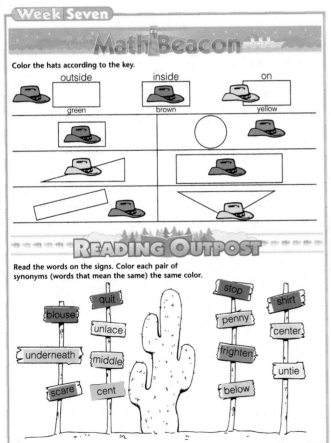

READING OUTPOST

Read the words on the signs. Color each pair of synonyms (words that mean the same) the same color.

blouse
quit
unlace
underneath
middle
scare
cent

stop
penny
frighten
below

shirt
center
untie

78   ···· DAY **3** ····

Write an equation for each word problem.
Solve it.

Robert has 7 tents.
Ed has 3 tents.
How many more tents does Robert have than Ed?

| 7 | − | 3 | = | 4 | tents |

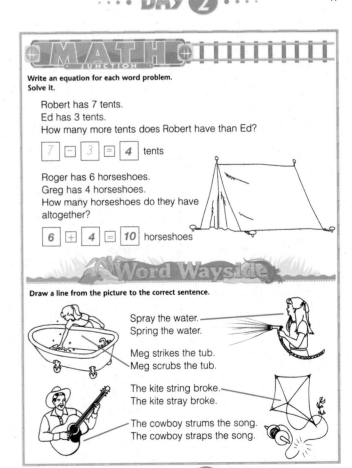

Roger has 6 horseshoes.
Greg has 4 horseshoes.
How many horseshoes do they have altogether?

| 6 | + | 4 | = | 10 | horseshoes |

Word Wayside

Draw a line from the picture to the correct sentence.

Spray the water.
Spring the water.

Meg strikes the tub.
Meg scrubs the tub.

The kite string broke.
The kite stray broke.

The cowboy strums the song.
The cowboy straps the song.

···· DAY **3** ····   79

READING OUTPOST

Read each sentence and question. Circle the correct answer.

1. The baby can (crawl.)
   What can the baby do?

2. The horse has a (saddle) on its back.
   What does the horse have on its back?

3. (Clouds) are in the sky.
   What are in the sky?

4. The (horse) ran into the hills.
   What ran into the hills?

5. The (grass) in the field is turning green.
   What is turning green?

STUDY SKILL
HEADQUARTERS

Use the items from the pencil to fill in the lists.

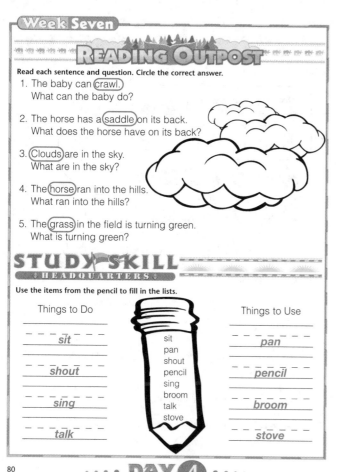

Things to Do		Things to Use
sit		pan
shout		pencil
sing		broom
talk		stove

Pencil contents: sit, pan, shout, pencil, sing, broom, talk, stove

DAY 4

Math Beacon

Circle the longest object.
Put an X on the shortest object.

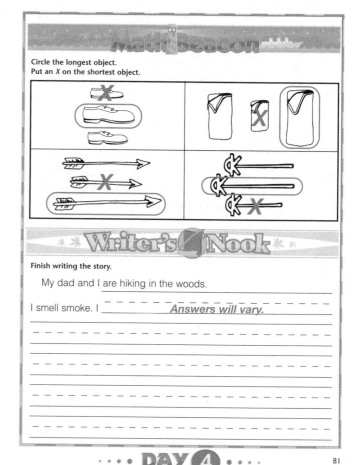

Writer's Nook

Finish writing the story.

My dad and I are hiking in the woods.

I smell smoke. I _____ *Answers will vary.*

DAY 4

MATH JUNCTION

Solve each problem using the place-value frame.

Tens	Ones
4	7
− 1	7
3	0

Tens	Ones
8	8
− 4	7
4	1

Tens	Ones
3	7
− 2	5
1	2

Tens	Ones
7	2
− 5	1
2	1

Tens	Ones
9	1
− 8	0
1	1

Tens	Ones
2	3
− 1	3
1	0

LANGUAGE LODGE

Put *F* if the sentence is fanciful.
Put *T* if the sentence could be true.

_F_ 1. The prairie dogs talked about the hawk.

_T_ 2. The horse galloped down the trail.

_F_ 3. Billy Bookworm ate part of the book.

_F_ 4. The cow jumped over the moon.

_T_ 5. All our family will go to the park.

_T_ 6. The elephant sprayed water on me.

DAY 5

READING OUTPOST

Draw a picture of the sentence.

The cowboy feeds the cattle.

Fact Harbor

Complete each family of facts.

9	+	4	=	13
4	+	9	=	13
13	−	9	=	4
13	−	4	=	9

9	+	6	=	15
6	+	9	=	15
15	−	9	=	6
15	−	6	=	9

DAY 5

STATION BREAK

Accept any reasonable answers.

Circle the things wrong in the picture.

MATH JUNCTION

Write an equation for each word problem. Solve.

Carl has 4 sacks of grain. Dan has 5 sacks of grain. Randy has 6 sacks of grain. How many sacks are there?

| 4 | + | 5 | + | 6 | = | 15 | sacks |

Kristy wants 2 hamburgers. Jason wants 2 hamburgers. Uncle Will wants 3 hamburgers. How many hamburgers need to be made?

| 2 | + | 2 | + | 3 | = | 7 | hamburgers |

Word Wayside

Write the vowel sound you hear in each picture.

ā   ē   ī   ō   ū

$\bar{i}$ $\bar{o}$

$\bar{a}$ $\bar{e}$

$\bar{u}$ $\bar{i}$

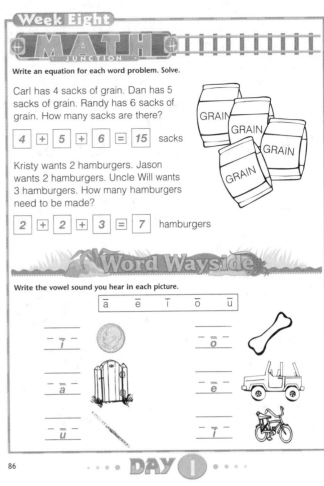

DAY 1

Math Beacon

Circle the correct number in each set.

$\frac{1}{half}$	
$\frac{1}{fourth}$	
$\frac{1}{third}$	
$\frac{1}{fourth}$	
$\frac{1}{half}$	

READING OUTPOST

Read each word family.
Draw a line from the picture to the correct word.

bite
kite
white

flight
sight
bright

might
right
light

write
bite
quite

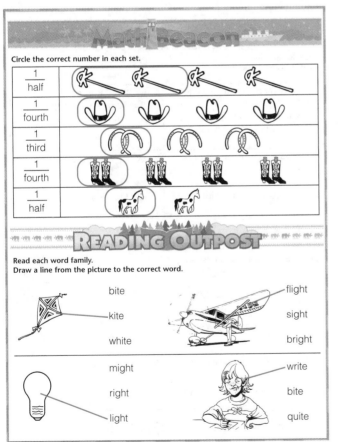

DAY 1

The American Bison

The bison is one of the biggest animals in the West. It has a huge head with horns. It also has a large hump on its back. Most bison are dark brown or black.

Bison live in herds. They feed on the grass of the plains. They also eat small shrubs.

Long ago, Native Americans hunted bison. They ate bison meat. They also made shoes from its hide. They used its horns to make arrows. Today most bison live on the plains of the West. You might also see them at the zoo.

Write the answers.

1. The bison has a huge head with _____ *horns* _____.

2. What color are most bison? _____ *dark brown or black* _____

3. What did Native Americans use bison for? _____
   _____ *possible answers: to eat, to make shoes or arrows* _____

4. Where do most bison live today? _____ *out west or in a zoo* _____

5. Why is the West a good place for bison to live?
   _____
   _____ *Accept any answer.* _____

DAY 2

Write the missing months.

| November | July | March | January | June | September |

| --- | --- | --- |
January	May	September
February	June	October
March	July	November
April	August	December

Word Wayside

Divide each underlined word into syllables.

Example: c l a s s • e s

1. The cowboy is w a l k • i n g to his horse.
2. The cactus was t a l l • e r than Kevin.
3. The rodeo is s o o n • e r than the fair.
4. The deer r e s t • e d by the fence.
5. The pines are t a l l • e r than the oaks.
6. Linda was r e a d • i n g when Mom called her.

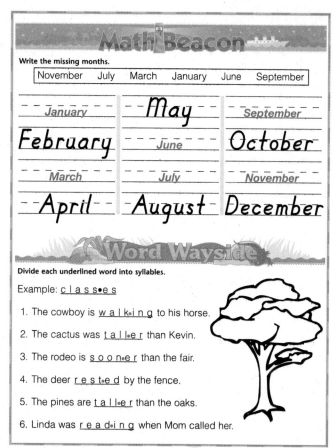

· · · · DAY 2 · · · ·

89

Complete the number sentence with = or ≠.

70 + 4 ≠ 75   40 + 5 = 45
30 + 6 ≠ 39   20 + 7 ≠ 26
10 + 8 ≠ 19   90 + 6 = 96
50 + 3 = 53   60 + 5 ≠ 64
20 + 2 ≠ 21   80 + 4 = 84
90 + 3 = 93   30 + 8 ≠ 39
60 + 8 ≠ 69   70 + 1 = 71

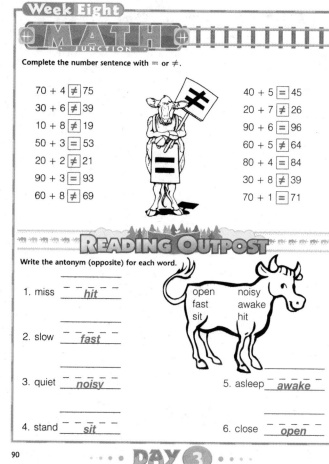

READING OUTPOST

Write the antonym (opposite) for each word.

open	noisy
fast	awake
sit	hit

1. miss _hit_

2. slow _fast_

3. quiet _noisy_

4. stand _sit_

5. asleep _awake_

6. close _open_

· · · · DAY 3 · · · ·

90

Fact Harbor

Solve each fact.
Color the boxes red that have 8 as the answer.

17 −8 = 9	14 −7 = 7	13 −5 = 8
11 −6 = 5	16 −8 = 8	10 −8 = 2
15 −7 = 8	12 −8 = 4	18 −9 = 9

Word Wayside

Draw lines to match the words and the pictures.

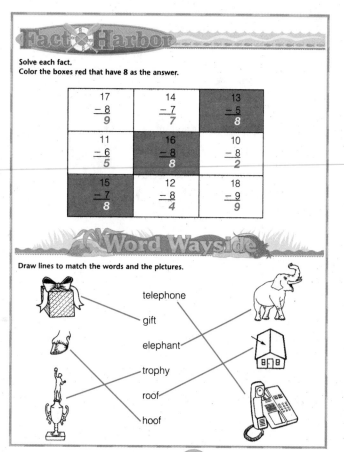

telephone

gift

elephant

trophy

roof

hoof

· · · · DAY 3 · · · ·

91

Read the sentences.
Mark the correct answers.

1. Terry mopped up the water for Mother.
   ● Terry was helpful.
   ○ Terry was not helpful.

2. Meg won the sprint.
   ● Meg is a fast runner.
   ○ Meg is a slow runner.

3. Mike thanked the coach for giving him the trophy.
   ○ Mike was selfish.
   ● Mike was thankful.

4. Mark planted flowers for Mrs. Tomkins.
   ● Mark was kind.
   ○ Mark was angry.

STUDY SKILL HEADQUARTERS

Use the map to complete each sentence.

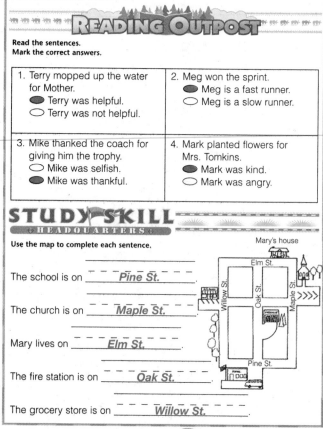

The school is on _Pine St._

The church is on _Maple St._

Mary lives on _Elm St._

The fire station is on _Oak St._

The grocery store is on _Willow St._

· · · · DAY 4 · · · ·

92

Math Beacon

Circle which holds more.

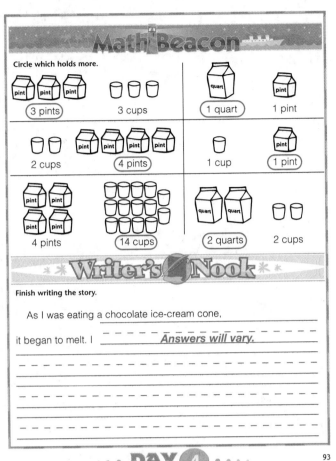

Writer's Nook

Finish writing the story.

As I was eating a chocolate ice-cream cone,

it began to melt. I _____ ___ ___ ___ ___ ___
Answers will vary.

_____ ___ ___ ___ ___ ___ ___

_____ ___ ___ ___ ___ ___ ___

_____ ___ ___ ___ ___ ___ ___

_____ ___ ___ ___ ___ ___ ___

Math Beacon

Draw what comes next.

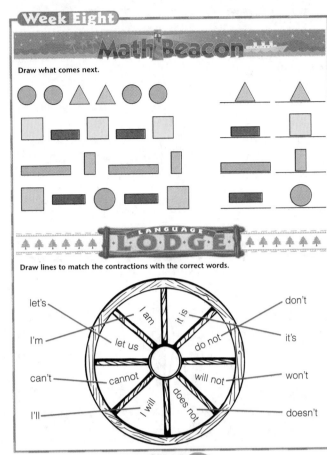

LANGUAGE LODGE

Draw lines to match the contractions with the correct words.

let's — I am
I'm — let us
can't — cannot
I'll — I will
it is — don't
do not — it's
will not — won't
does not — doesn't

READING OUTPOST

Draw a picture of the sentence.

The rattlesnake crawled in the weeds.

Fact Harbor

Complete each family of facts.

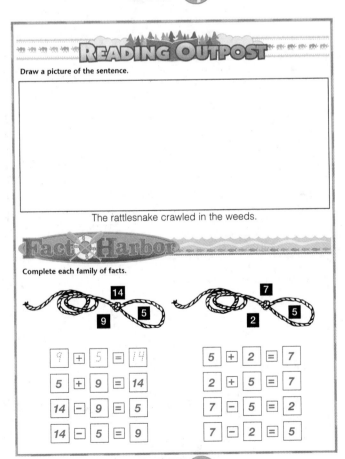

$$9 + 5 = 14$$
$$5 + 9 = 14$$
$$14 - 9 = 5$$
$$14 - 5 = 9$$

$$5 + 2 = 7$$
$$2 + 5 = 7$$
$$7 - 5 = 2$$
$$7 - 2 = 5$$

Week 8 · STATION BREAK

Read each clue.
Find the words that tell you about a cowboy and his horse.

Down
1. what you can put a saddle on
2. what a horse wears on its feet
3. what you put on a horse's back

Across
4. a rope
5. wheels attached to the heels of a rider's boots
6. the long hair on a horse's neck

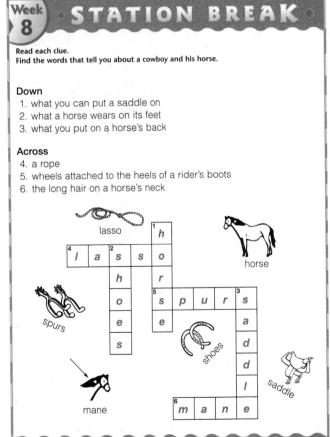

lasso

horse

spurs

shoes

saddle

mane

Fact Harbor

Solve the facts.

$$2 + 7 = 9$$
$$2 + 9 = 11$$
$$6 + 5 = 11$$
$$6 + 3 = 9$$

$$3 + 8 = 11$$
$$3 + 4 = 7$$
$$4 + 4 = 8$$
$$4 + 2 = 6$$

$$5 + 6 = 11$$
$$5 + 0 = 5$$
$$8 + 9 = 17$$
$$8 + 8 = 16$$

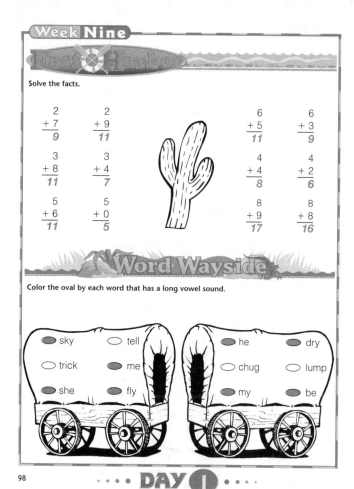

Word Wayside

Color the oval by each word that has a long vowel sound.

- ● sky   ○ tell
- ○ trick   ● me
- ● she   ● fly

- ● he   ● dry
- ○ chug   ○ lump
- ● my   ● be

DAY 1

MATH JUNCTION

Write the number of tens and ones.

20 _2_ tens _0_ ones   68 _6_ tens _8_ ones

39 _3_ tens _9_ ones   72 _7_ tens _2_ ones

93 _9_ tens _3_ ones   47 _4_ tens _7_ ones

51 _5_ tens _1_ ones   19 _1_ tens _9_ ones

85 _8_ tens _5_ ones   89 _8_ tens _9_ ones

READING OUTPOST

Put an X on the word that does not belong in the word family.

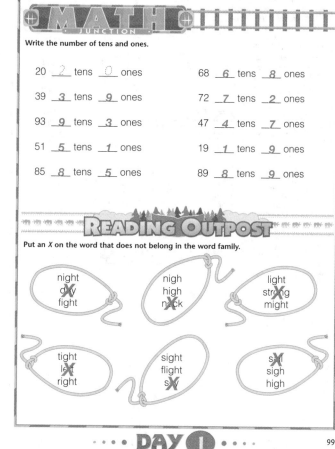

- night, d**X**y, fight
- nigh, high, n**X**ck
- light, str**X**ng, might
- tight, l**X**, right
- sight, flight, s**X**
- s**X**, sigh, high

DAY 1

The Sod House

Jenny stood by the door of the sod house. She looked up at the sky. Black clouds were rolling in from the west. A raindrop fell on her nose. Jenny went back inside. "Papa, will we be safe?"

Papa pulled the door shut. "The roof is sound," he said. "The walls are strong. We will be safe in our sod house. God brought us here to Nebraska. He will take care of us."

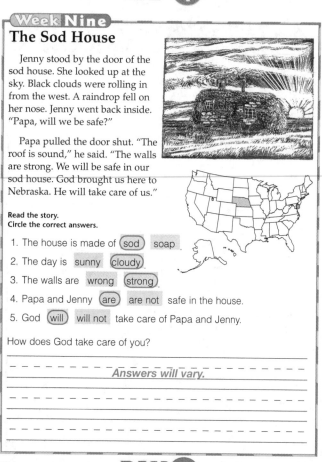

Read the story.
Circle the correct answers.

1. The house is made of (sod) soap.

2. The day is sunny (cloudy).

3. The walls are wrong (strong).

4. Papa and Jenny (are) are not safe in the house.

5. God (will) will not take care of Papa and Jenny.

How does God take care of you?

_____
Answers will vary.
_____

DAY 2

MATH JUNCTION

Write an equation for each word problem.
Solve it.

Tasha has 25¢.
Her dad gives her 20¢.
How much money does Tasha have in all?

| 25¢ | + | 20¢ | = | 45 | ¢ |

Aunt Ellen gave Tim 32¢.
Uncle Carl gave him 21¢.
How much money does Tim have in all?

| 32¢ | + | 21¢ | = | 53 | ¢ |

Work Space

Word Wayside

Put a letter in each boot and add a suffix.
Draw a line from each picture to the correct word.

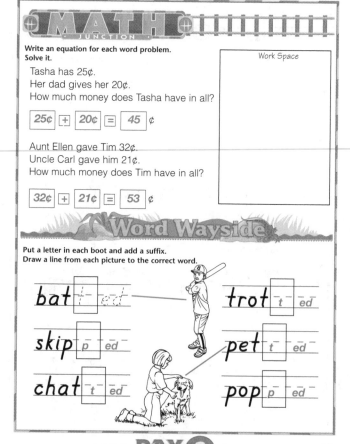

bat [t] [ed]   trot [t] [ed]

skip [p] [ed]   pet [t] [ed]

chat [t] [ed]   pop [p] [ed]

DAY 2

Math Beacon

Divide the shapes into equal parts.

Halves			
Thirds			
Fourths			

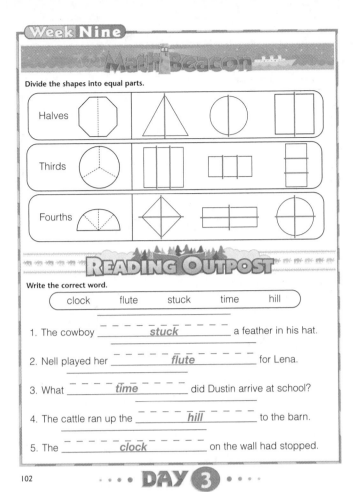

READING OUTPOST

Write the correct word.

| clock | flute | stuck | time | hill |

1. The cowboy _____**stuck**_____ a feather in his hat.

2. Nell played her _____**flute**_____ for Lena.

3. What _____**time**_____ did Dustin arrive at school?

4. The cattle ran up the _____**hill**_____ to the barn.

5. The _____**clock**_____ on the wall had stopped.

DAY 3

Hac Harbor

Solve the facts.

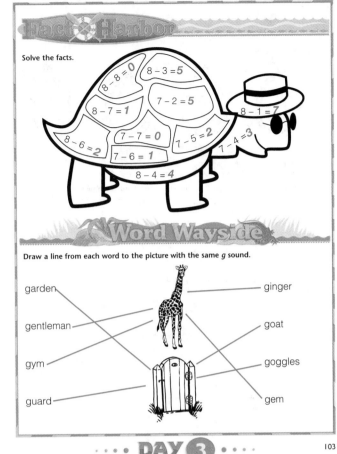

$$8 - 8 = 0$$
$$8 - 3 = 5$$
$$8 - 7 = 1$$
$$7 - 2 = 5$$
$$8 - 1 = 7$$
$$7 - 7 = 0$$
$$7 - 5 = 2$$
$$7 - 4 = 3$$
$$8 - 6 = 2$$
$$7 - 6 = 1$$
$$8 - 4 = 4$$

Word Wayside

Draw a line from each word to the picture with the same g sound.

garden   ginger

gentleman   goat

gym   goggles

guard   gem

READING OUTPOST

Draw a line from the picture to the correct sentence.

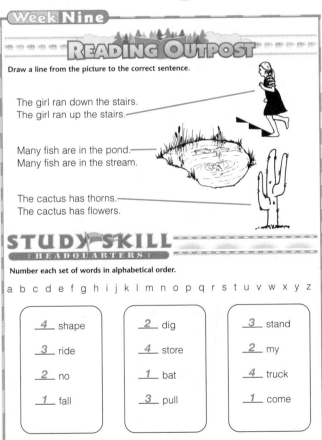

The girl ran down the stairs.
The girl ran up the stairs.

Many fish are in the pond.
Many fish are in the stream.

The cactus has thorns.
The cactus has flowers.

STUDY SKILL
HEADQUARTERS

Number each set of words in alphabetical order.

a b c d e f g h i j k l m n o p q r s t u v w x y z

_4_ shape	_2_ dig	_3_ stand
_3_ ride	_4_ store	_2_ my
_2_ no	_1_ bat	_4_ truck
_1_ fall	_3_ pull	_1_ come

DAY 4

Math Beacon

Put an X on the boxes with objects holding less than one liter.
Color the boxes with objects holding more than one liter.

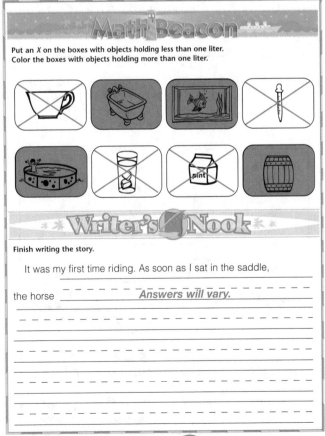

Writer's Nook

Finish writing the story.

It was my first time riding. As soon as I sat in the saddle,

the horse _____**Answers will vary.**_____

MATH JUNCTION

Solve each problem.

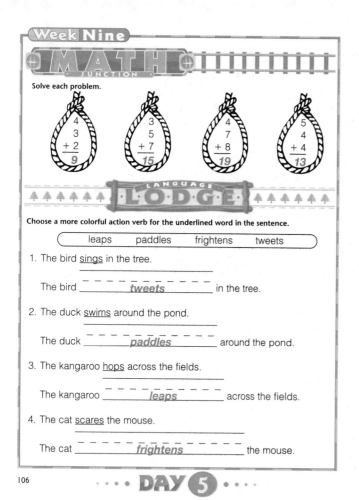

$$\begin{array}{r} 4 \\ 3 \\ +\ 2 \\ \hline 9 \end{array} \qquad \begin{array}{r} 3 \\ 5 \\ +\ 7 \\ \hline 15 \end{array} \qquad \begin{array}{r} 4 \\ 7 \\ +\ 8 \\ \hline 19 \end{array} \qquad \begin{array}{r} 5 \\ 4 \\ +\ 4 \\ \hline 13 \end{array}$$

LANGUAGE LODGE

Choose a more colorful action verb for the underlined word in the sentence.

| leaps | paddles | frightens | tweets |

1. The bird <u>sings</u> in the tree.

   The bird _____ *tweets* _____ in the tree.

2. The duck <u>swims</u> around the pond.

   The duck _____ *paddles* _____ around the pond.

3. The kangaroo <u>hops</u> across the fields.

   The kangaroo _____ *leaps* _____ across the fields.

4. The cat <u>scares</u> the mouse.

   The cat _____ *frightens* _____ the mouse.

106 · · · · **DAY 5** · · · ·

READING OUTPOST

Draw a picture of the sentence.

The saddle is too big for the pony.

Fact Harbor

Complete each family of facts.

7	+	4	=	11
4	+	7	=	11
11	−	7	=	4
11	−	4	=	7

4	+	2	=	6
2	+	4	=	6
6	−	4	=	2
6	−	2	=	4

· · · · **DAY 5** · · · · 107

STATION BREAK

Put an *X* on the picture that is the same as the first picture.

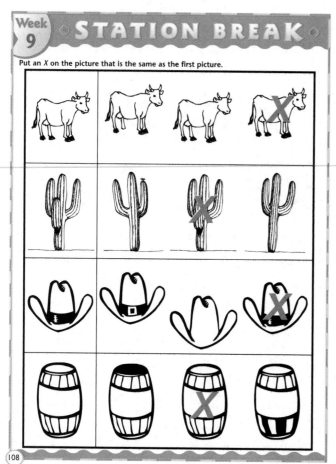

108

Fact Harbor

Solve the facts to read the message.

$$\begin{array}{r} 1 \\ +\ 6 \\ \hline 7 \end{array}\ \text{D} \qquad \begin{array}{r} 3 \\ +\ 7 \\ \hline 10 \end{array}\ \text{O} \qquad \begin{array}{r} 3 \\ +\ 9 \\ \hline 12 \end{array}\ \text{U} \qquad \begin{array}{r} 4 \\ +\ 2 \\ \hline 6 \end{array}\ \text{V} \qquad \begin{array}{r} 4 \\ +\ 7 \\ \hline 11 \end{array}\ \text{E}$$

$$\begin{array}{r} 7 \\ +\ 7 \\ \hline 14 \end{array}\ \text{L} \qquad \begin{array}{r} 0 \\ +\ 8 \\ \hline 8 \end{array}\ \text{Y} \qquad \begin{array}{r} 4 \\ +\ 9 \\ \hline 13 \end{array}\ \text{S} \qquad \begin{array}{r} 3 \\ +\ 1 \\ \hline 4 \end{array}\ \text{G}$$

G O D   L O V E S   Y O U
4 10 7   14 10 6 11 13   8 10 12

Word Wayside

Write the vowel sound you hear in the middle of the words.

a bl_a_ck m_a_ne   a p_a_n with a l_i_d

a p_i_g in a b_o_x   a d_o_g with a b_o_ne

110 · · · · **DAY 1** · · · ·

Count by 2s, 5s, and 10s. Write the missing numbers.

54	*56*	58	*60*	*62*	64	*66*	68	*70*	*72*
74	76	*78*	80	*82*	84	*86*	88	90	*92*

5	*10*	*15*	20	25	*30*	*35*	*40*	45	*50*
55	60	*65*	*70*	75	*80*	85	*90*	95	*100*

10	*20*	*30*	40	*50*	60	*70*	80	*90*	100

READING OUTPOST

Write the correct word.

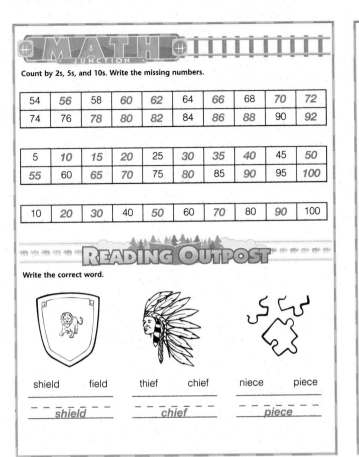

shield   field

thief   chief

niece   piece

_ _ _ _ _ _ _
shield

_ _ _ _ _ _ _
chief

_ _ _ _ _ _ _
piece

· · · · **DAY 1** · · · ·

111

My Pony and Me

We make a fine pair,
My pony and me.
We both wear our (hair)
Hanging long, loose, and free.

He loves to run,
And I love to ride.
We both think it's fun
To spend all day outside—

To trot up the lane
Past the old tool shed
With the wind in our mane
And the sky straight ahead.

Follow the instructions.

1. Circle the word in the poem that rhymes with *pair*.

2. Why does the rider like to be outside?

   She likes to ride her pony.
   _ _ _ _ _ _ _ _ _

3. Where could you ride your pony?

   Answers will vary.
   _ _ _ _ _ _ _ _ _
   _ _ _ _ _ _ _ _ _

In the box above, draw a picture of yourself riding a pony.

112   · · · · **DAY 2** · · · ·

Math Beacon

Circle the correct time.

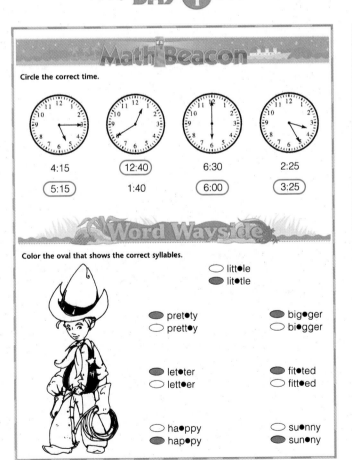

4:15
(5:15)

(12:40)
1:40

6:30
(6:00)

2:25
(3:25)

Word Wayside

Color the oval that shows the correct syllables.

- ○ litt•le
- ● lit•tle

- ● pret•ty
- ○ prett•y

- ● big•ger
- ○ bi•gger

- ● let•ter
- ○ lett•er

- ● fit•ted
- ○ fitt•ed

- ○ ha•ppy
- ● hap•py

- ○ su•nny
- ● sun•ny

· · · · **DAY 2** · · · ·

113

Math Beacon

Write the fraction for the colored part.

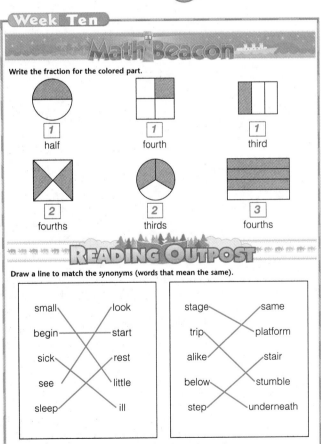

1	*1*	*1*
half	fourth	third

2	*2*	*3*
fourths	thirds	fourths

READING OUTPOST

Draw a line to match the synonyms (words that mean the same).

small — little
begin — start
sick — ill
see — look
sleep — rest

stage — platform
trip — stumble
alike — same
below — underneath
step — stair

114   · · · · **DAY 3** · · · ·

Solve the facts.

$$\begin{array}{r} 15 \\ -9 \\ \hline 6 \end{array} \qquad \begin{array}{r} 14 \\ -7 \\ \hline 7 \end{array} \qquad \begin{array}{r} 15 \\ -7 \\ \hline 8 \end{array} \qquad \begin{array}{r} 15 \\ -6 \\ \hline 9 \end{array}$$

$$\begin{array}{r} 14 \\ -6 \\ \hline 8 \end{array} \qquad \begin{array}{r} 14 \\ -8 \\ \hline 6 \end{array} \qquad \begin{array}{r} 14 \\ -9 \\ \hline 5 \end{array}$$

$$\begin{array}{r} 16 \\ -8 \\ \hline 8 \end{array} \qquad \begin{array}{r} 16 \\ -9 \\ \hline 7 \end{array} \qquad \begin{array}{r} 16 \\ -7 \\ \hline 9 \end{array} \qquad \begin{array}{r} 15 \\ -8 \\ \hline 7 \end{array}$$

Word Wayside

Add the correct blend to name the picture.

gr	pr	tr

_**tr**_ ain

_**gr**_ apes

_**pr**_ ize

_**tr**_ ee

_**gr**_ andfather

_**pr**_ ince

READING OUTPOST

Read the sentences. Circle the answer.

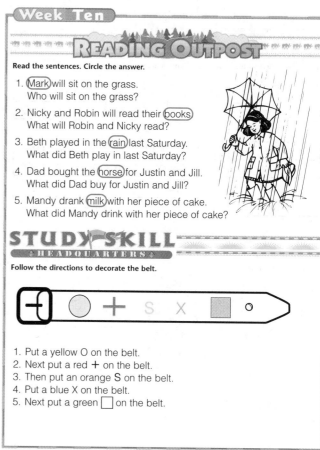

1. (Mark) will sit on the grass.
   Who will sit on the grass?

2. Nicky and Robin will read their (books)
   What will Robin and Nicky read?

3. Beth played in the (rain) last Saturday.
   What did Beth play in last Saturday?

4. Dad bought the (horse) for Justin and Jill.
   What did Dad buy for Justin and Jill?

5. Mandy drank (milk) with her piece of cake.
   What did Mandy drink with her piece of cake?

STUDY SKILL
HEADQUARTERS

Follow the directions to decorate the belt.

1. Put a yellow O on the belt.
2. Next put a red + on the belt.
3. Then put an orange S on the belt.
4. Put a blue X on the belt.
5. Next put a green ☐ on the belt.

Math Beacon

Write the number of inches.

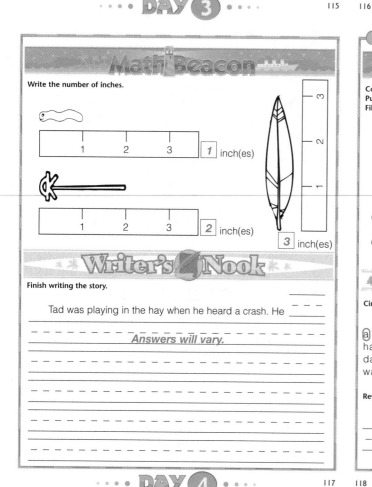

1	2	3

1 inch(es)

1	2	3

2 inch(es)

3 inch(es)

Writer's Nook

Finish writing the story.

Tad was playing in the hay when he heard a crash. He _____

Answers will vary.

Math Beacon

Color the circle on each corner.
Put an X on each side.
Fill in the boxes.

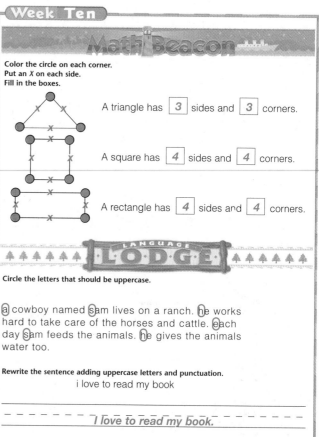

A triangle has **3** sides and **3** corners.

A square has **4** sides and **4** corners.

A rectangle has **4** sides and **4** corners.

LANGUAGE LODGE

Circle the letters that should be uppercase.

(a) cowboy named (s)am lives on a ranch. (h)e works hard to take care of the horses and cattle. (e)ach day (s)am feeds the animals. (h)e gives the animals water too.

Rewrite the sentence adding uppercase letters and punctuation.
i love to read my book

I love to read my book.

READING OUTPOST

Draw a picture of the sentence.

The rainbow shone over the field.

MATH JUNCTION

**Write an equation for each word problem.
Solve it.**

Tom had 7 baseball cards.
Bobby had 6 baseball cards.
How many baseball cards do
they have together?

| 7 | + | 6 | = | 13 | baseball cards

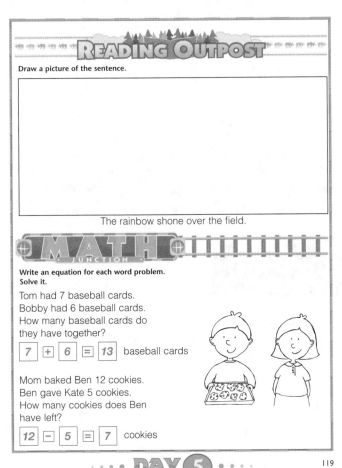

Mom baked Ben 12 cookies.
Ben gave Kate 5 cookies.
How many cookies does Ben
have left?

| 12 | − | 5 | = | 7 | cookies

···· **DAY 5** ····

119

Complete the other half of the picture.
Decorate and color.

120

Finally—